# NATURE GUIDES

## Gathering and using information helps us understand and describe the natural world.

SCHOLASTIC

LITERACY
PLACE ™

Copyright acknowledgments and credits appear on page 128, which constitutes an extension of this copyright page.

Copyright © 1996 by Scholastic Inc.          All rights reserved.          Printed in the U.S.A.
                                             ISBN 0-590-49126-1
          5 6 7 8 9 10                       24                 02 01 00 99 98 97

# Explore
## a National Park

Gathering and
using information
help us understand
and describe the
natural world.

# Nature Notes

## We can observe and describe the natural world.

Crab spider on
milkweed leaf
waiting fr prey.
Has no web.
Changes color to
surrounding

I 1½"

August
North H
10:30 am
mid 700's
breezy. sunny
fields browning
over but still
lush
hear =
di

# SECTION 2

# Wild Things

## Writers create a picture of nature through their words.

# Take a Hike!

## Each environment tells its own story about nature.

# Trade Books

## The following books accompany this *Nature Guides* SourceBook.

Newbery Honor
### Classic Fiction

### Charlotte's Web

by E.B. White
illustrated by
Garth Williams

### Nonfiction

AWARD WINNING Book

### Come Back, Salmon

by Molly Cone
photographed
by Sidnee
Wheelwright

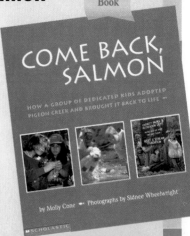

### Biography

AWARD WINNING Book

### Listening to Crickets: A Story about Rachel Carson

by Candice F.
Ransom
illustrated by
Shelly O. Haas

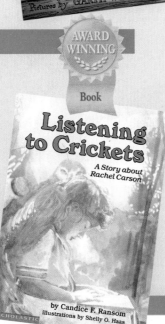

### Fiction

### The Secret of the Seal

by Deborah Davis
illustrated by
Judy Labrasca

Bison

Old Faithful

Larkspur

Elk refuge

Fawn

We can observe and describe
the natural world.

# Nature Notes

Explore the swampy
Everglades through
the watchful eyes of
an alligator. Then get
the facts on this
endangered reptile.

Follow park ranger
Veronica Gonzales-
Vest on a nature trail
through an animal
sanctuary.

Hike through a
national park with
Ali Baba and keep a
lookout for bears.

## WORKSHOP 1

In your nature log, record
observations of a favorite
outdoor place.

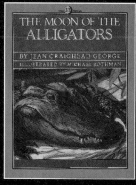

THE MOON OF THE
ALLIGATORS

BY JEAN CRAIGHEAD GEORGE
ILLUSTRATED BY MICHAEL ROTHMAN

Environmental
Fiction

FROM

# THE MOON OF THE ALLIGATORS

Book

By JEAN CRAIGHEAD GEORGE

Illustrated by MICHAEL ROTHMAN

Two eyes poked above the still water. Each iris was silver-yellow and each pupil black and narrow. They were the eyes of the alligator of Sawgrass Hole, who was floating like a log on the surface of the water as she watched for food. She saw the blue sky above her, and because her eyes were on the top and to the rear of her head, she saw all the way behind her to the tall cypress trees. Their limbs spread like silver wires above a tangle of sweet bay and buttonbushes.

The alligator did not move, but watched and waited even though hunger gnawed her belly.

She had eaten little since June, when the rainy season had flooded her home and the prey she fed upon had swum away. Now her sense of seasonal rhythm told her that the afternoon's cloudless sky meant the end of the rains and hurricanes, and the return of the wildlife to her water hole. The moon of October was the beginning of southern Florida's dry season. The water level would fall. The fish, frogs, turtles, and birds would come back to Sawgrass Hole, where she lived. They would be followed by the herons and ibis, egrets, anhinga or water turkeys, and she would eat well once more.

She was in her pool in the Everglades of Florida, which is not a swamp as it is often called, but a river like none other in the world. The Everglades does not flow—it seeps. Forty to sixty miles wide and a hundred miles long, it creeps, like glistening quicksilver, from Lake Okeechobee southward across a flat limestone bed to the Florida Bay. The Everglades is not only a river, but also a wet prairie. Saw grass, that rugged plant whose grasslike leaves are edged with sharp spines, grows like a crop from shore to shore. Rising out of the saw grass are tree islands, known as hammocks, where a variety of trees grow. Other islands are forests of bay, called "heads," buttonwood and cypress trees.

The Everglades and its plants and creatures, including the alligator, have adapted to the wet and dry seasons of the semitropical zone in south Florida. When the river is high in summer's wet season, little fish, like guppies and gambusia that eat mosquito larvae, swim among the saw grass stalks far out in the river. They dodge the largemouth bass and sunfish, who, in turn, avoid the Florida soft-shelled turtle.

During the winter season when the river is low, the wildlife of the Everglades adjusts to dryness. As the water level drops, and just before the river bottom becomes exposed to the sun and cracks, the river creatures come to the alligator holes. They live through the drought of winter in these watery sanctuaries.

October was always a critical time for the alligators as they waited for their food to return. In this century, however, the month of October has become a near disaster for them. Human-made canals, dug into the limestone to drain the Everglades for farming, have killed off millions and billions of frogs, fish, birds, mammals, and turtles. Their food depleted, the alligators died in huge numbers from starvation. In addition, hunters killed tens of thousands for their valuable skins. The passing of the alligators threatened all the wildlife in the Everglades, for their holes are oases for life during the dry season. The great flocks of beautiful birds were reduced to a few. Fish and turtles died out for lack of winter retreats. The alligator, people began to realize, was the "farmer" that kept the chain of life going.

In the 1970s there were so few American alligators left on this earth that Congress declared it an endangered species, one that is doomed to extinction and would be protected by law. Since that decree, the big reptiles have made a strong comeback in their original homeland that stretches from Texas to North Carolina. They are now only a threatened species.

The six-foot alligator of Sawgrass Hole did not know about her status, she only knew her belly ached. Sinking to the bottom of the pool, she looked for food. The river was getting low. A few minnows too small to bother with darted past her. A measly pollywog rested in the warm mud.

She ignored it, whipped her tail from side to side, and then circled her large home. The water was filling with algae, one-celled plants that grow profusely in the sun. Long strips of these green plants floated in scummy masses. They bothered her.

With a powerful thrust from her tail she drove her body into a patch of algae and caught it on her nose. Swimming with surprising grace, she carried it to the shore and pushed it up with her nose and feet, then returned and bulldozed another load ashore. Next she went to the overgrown water lilies floating on the surface. Taking a plant in her mouth, she tugged it across the pool and dragged it up on land to die.

When she was done she could see the minnows more clearly, and the minnows, freed from the weeds, flickered back and forth across Sawgrass Hole eating microscopic food called periphyton. In the days that followed, they grew rapidly and larger fish fed on them. For the alligator, however, there was no food big enough for her to bother with.

Her hole, which was fifteen feet deep and some forty feet long and wide, was far out in the Everglades at the edge of a cypress head. On one of its shores was a beach where she sunbathed. Around the edges of the pool in the shallow water grew pickerelweed and arrow-heads. Among their stems the fry of the largemouth bass grew up. On the shore, just out of the water, grew clumps of six-foot-tall alligator flags. Their large leaves, on the ends of long stalks, waved and fluttered like banners. These plants announce the locations of alligator homes to human, bird, and beast. When the big reptiles are killed or die, the plants die too, for there is no alligator-farmer to weed. The algae multiply and clog the pools, weeds take over the shallows and shore and, finally, trees and bushes fill in the pond, choking out the alligator flags.

One evening the big 'gator lay near the shore watching the bushes. The moon of October was working its change. The water in the river was lowering, and the fish and wildlife were coming to her deep hole. A snowy egret alighted on a limb of a pop ash near the water. The bird no longer held his feathers close to his body as he did in summer, but lifted them slightly to let his delicate plumes float down the back of his neck like a veil. The moon of October is the beginning of the breeding season for the egrets. In a month or so he would strut for his mate, spread his plumes, then bow and dance for her.

The egret picked up a stick, held it a moment, then dropped it. It was a present for his mate, but he was not quite ready to give it to her. October was a time to practice the art of courtship, and practice he did. He picked up another stick. The alligator eyed him but did not stalk. He was too high in the tree to catch.

The bird flew, his yellow feet and black legs gleaming as he skimmed over Sawgrass Hole and climbed into the air. High over the 'gator hole, he turned and headed for his rookery on a buttonwood island near the Florida Bay. The 'gator watched him until he was out of sight, then submerged herself in the river. She made no ripples to alarm her prey, nor did she disturb the waters as she pressed her huge jaws together. They closed over seventy sharp white teeth, forming the perpetual grin of an alligator. Her tail, almost half of her length, torpedoed her across the pool to the shore where the cypress trees grew. As she came up on land, water spilled from her sculptured armor and her third eyelid pulled back to let her see in the air.

The alligator saw movement beneath a pop ash. Rising to her feet on short legs, she peered into a brushy jungle that she and her ancestors had created. For a thousand years the alligators of Sawgrass Hole had made land by weeding and piling the debris on this shore. Tree seeds had rooted in the rich compost. The seedlings had grown into a sheltering jungle that attracted rabbits, raccoons, bobcats, and river otter.

The 'gator lunged at a marsh rabbit who was nibbling on leaves. He had been born in late summer. With the rise of the moon of October he had left home to seek his fortune. He had not gone far before he came upon the alligator's jungle and, finding it rich with rabbit food, settled in. Blackish-brown in color, he looked like the cotton-tail rabbits of the north, except that he had no white on his tail. However, he did possess their ability to leap, and before the alligator could lunge a second time, he had catapulted over her tail and plunged into the pool. He swam quickly across Sawgrass Hole and bounced ashore. Marsh rabbits are excellent swimmers.

Being so close to catching a rabbit made the alligator even hungrier. She dove into her pool and scanned the undersides of the bladderworts, floating plants that catch insects and take nourishment from them. No dark areas marked the bodies of resting frogs. They were still out in the glades. Patiently she waited.

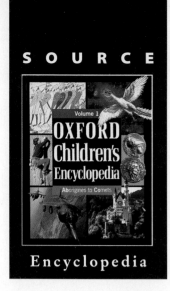
# ALLIGATORS

## Alligators

Alligators and their close relatives the caymans are short-snouted members of the crocodile family. True alligators seem to be able to survive in colder conditions than their relatives. They live further north and may hibernate during the winter.

Most species of cayman and alligator probably live and develop in much the same way as the much-studied American alligator. All species swim well and feed from the water on fish and mammals, and they all lay their eggs in sand. The Chinese alligator spends much time in a burrow dug into a river bank.

The skin of alligators and caymans makes valuable leather, and many have been destroyed because of this. In some cases the disappearance of these animals has led to ecological disaster, as the insects, rodents and fish on which they feed have increased in number and become pests. ■

## Chinese alligator

## American crocodile

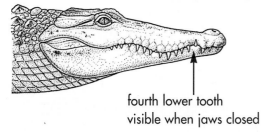

fourth lower tooth
visible when jaws closed

▲ Alligators have shorter, blunter snouts than crocodiles. When a crocodile's mouth is closed, the large tooth fourth from the center on the lower jaw still shows near the front of the mouth and fits into a notch in the upper jaw. No lower teeth can be seen when an alligator shuts its mouth.

### DISTRIBUTION

The American alligator is found in the warm parts of the southern United States and as far north as North Carolina. The Chinese alligator lives by the lower Chang Jiang (Yangtze) River. Caymans live in tropical parts of Central and South America.

**LARGEST** about 5.8 m

**NUMBER OF EGGS** 25–55

**LIFESPAN** 56 years in captivity

**SUBPHYLUM** Vertebrata

**CLASS** Reptilia

**ORDER** Crocodilia

**NUMBER OF SPECIES**
Alligators 2, caymans 5

The American alligator is likely to be seen by visitors to the Florida Everglades in the USA. At one time it was very rare, but because of conservation its numbers have now increased.

◄ Alligators spend much time basking in the sun or lying in wait for their prey. They swim by moving their long, powerful tails from side to side.

# Veronica Gonzales-Vest

## Park Ranger

**Park rangers see some wild things!**

Park ranger Veronica Gonzales-Vest works at the Sequoia National Park in California, which is famous for its giant trees. Sequoia trees are the largest living things in the world. Gonzales-Vest loves her job. She spends her days outdoors, patrolling the park and taking visitors on nature hikes.

## PROFILE

**Name:** Veronica Gonzales-Vest

**Occupation:** national park ranger

**What every park ranger needs:** a flashlight

**Favorite animal:** acorn woodpecker, because of the rat-a-tat sound it makes

**Significant park memory:** brought snow from the park to a school where the kids had never touched or smelled snow before

**Favorite vacation spot:** Santa Fe, New Mexico, where she grew up

# QUESTIONS
### for Veronica Gonzales-Vest

## Here's how one park ranger *manages* information *about* nature.

 **Do you use special tools to observe nature?**

 The tools I use are my eyes, ears, nose, hands, and brain. I use my senses—listening for birds, smelling wildflowers, and so on.

**Q** **How did you learn all the information about nature that you share with park visitors?**

**A** I learned by observing the wildlife in the park, and talking to other park rangers. I also read lots of reference books. That's why, when I take people on nature hikes, I can tell them about the plants and animals they'll see. And I warn them not to wander off. It's not part of the park experience to become lunch for a bear!

 **How do park rangers tell how old a sequoia tree is?**

 Park rangers are skilled at "reading the rings." They take a core sample from the tree and then count the rings from the center out. One light-colored ring plus one dark ring equals one year's growth. Sequoias can live to be 3,200 years old!

Pocket Guide to Songbirds

A Field Guide to Butterflies

North American WILD FLOWERS

**Q** What are some popular sites at Sequoia National Park?

**A** The Tunnel Log is a popular attraction. It was made from the trunk of a sequoia and is wide enough to drive a car through. After a visit to the tunnel, people can say they've driven through a tree. Another favorite site is the General Sherman tree. This tree is probably over 2,000 years old. (Imagine a cake with that many candles!) It's also *very* large. One of its branches is over 140 feet long!

**Q** Why do you think your job as a park ranger is important?

**A** There isn't anywhere else like Sequoia National Park. I love telling people about the park. I see kids' eyes light up when they learn new nature facts. Some of them may decide to become park rangers!

**Veronica Gonzales-Vest's**
## Tips **for Young Naturalists**

1 Use all your senses when observing nature.

2 Move quietly to avoid scaring the animals. You'll see more.

3 Be prepared. Carry a notebook and binoculars on your nature walks.

from
**Ali Baba Bernstein, Lost and Found**

AWARD
WINNING

Author

# Ali Baba
## Hunts for a Bear

# by Johanna Hurwitz
## illustrated by Michele Noiset

The summer after Ali Baba's tenth birthday, he and his parents went on a trip to Wyoming. When Mr. Bernstein first announced to his son that they were going to vacation in a couple of parks, Ali Baba thought he was making a joke.

The Bernsteins' apartment in New York City was near two parks—Riverside Park and Central Park. Both were nice places. When he was little, Ali Baba had played in the sandbox or on the swings and slides in the parks. It was good to have trees and grass in the middle of the city. But how could you take a vacation in the park?

"These parks are different," Mr. Bernstein explained to his son. "National parks are huge, and people come from all over the country to visit them."

"People come from all over the world," Ali Baba's mother added.

Ali Baba was sure they were exaggerating.

On the day that Ali Baba Bernstein was ten years, two months, and seven days old, they arrived in Grand Teton National Park in Wyoming. Then he saw that his parents had not been exaggerating at all. The park was huge. In fact, it looked bigger than Riverside Park and Central Park and a hundred other parks combined. And just as his parents had said, it was filled with thousands and thousands of tourists.

Some were Americans like Ali Baba. He began noticing the license plates on the cars. In the first hour in the park, he spotted plates from Illinois, Colorado, California, and Wyoming. The car that Mr. Bernstein had rented had license plates from Minnesota. When they stopped for lunch, a man came over to them.

"Whereabouts in Minnesota do you live?" he asked.

"We live in New York," said Mr. Bernstein, explaining
about the rented car.

"I was born in St. Paul, Minnesota," said the man.
"I thought you might come from there, too."

Ali Baba and his parents were staying in a little log
cabin. In the parking lot near the cabins, there were three
huge buses. The men and women coming out of the buses
looked just like Americans, but Ali Baba couldn't understand
a single word they said.

"What are they saying?" he asked his parents.

"I don't know," said Mrs. Bernstein. "They are speaking
German." Because she didn't know the language, she could
only guess what the people were talking about.

What most people seemed to be talking about were the animals. The park was filled with them. At home, the only animals Ali Baba ever saw in the park were squirrels and dogs. The dogs were supposed to be kept on leashes, but they often ran loose.

Here, there were herds of buffalo and antelope and deer. Sometimes you could see them very close to the road. Other times they were off in the distance.

Mr. Bernstein had brought a pair of binoculars, and Ali Baba kept busy searching for animals. He thought he would ask his father if he could borrow the binoculars when he got home. They seemed like very useful equipment for a would-be detective.

"I saw a bear," a girl told Ali Baba proudly as he was adjusting the binoculars at a lookout point the first morning.

"Where?" asked Ali Baba. He wondered if the girl was telling the truth. He hadn't seen any bears.

"Not here," said the girl. "When we were driving in Yellowstone National Park."

"Was it big?" asked Ali Baba.

"Huge," said the girl.

It seemed as if everything in the park was huge.

"Maybe I'll see a bear, too," said Ali Baba, putting the binoculars to his eyes.

"You probably won't," said the girl. "It's very hard to see them nowadays. My father said that when he came here twenty years ago, there were lots of bears."

"If you saw one, then I'll see one," said Ali Baba with certainty. He was determined to see a bear before he went back to New York City.

After that, Ali Baba spent all his time searching for a bear.

Mr. Bernstein took loads of pictures. He made Ali Baba smile into the camera at least a dozen times a day. Ali Baba found that very boring. It was embarrassing, too, if there were other people around. Most of the time, however, the other people were so busy posing and taking their own pictures that they didn't even notice.

"I see a bear!" Ali Baba shouted that afternoon.

"Where? Where?" asked his mother, looking around.

Mr. Bernstein grabbed his camera, ready to focus it at the elusive animal.

"Ha-ha! I made you look!" Ali Baba laughed. He had really fooled his parents.

"Do you remember the story of the boy who called wolf?" asked Mr. Bernstein. "If you try and trick us now, no one will believe you if you ever do see a real bear."

So Ali Baba kept watch for a bear. And he began to keep score of the animals he did see:

| | | | |
|---|---|---|---|
| moose | 17 | marmot | 1 |
| buffalo | 39 | antelope | 8 |
| beavers | 3 | deer | 12 |
| gophers | 61 | coyote | 1 |

He didn't bother to count mosquitoes. They had mosquitoes at home.

There were many things to do in the park. One morning, they got up extra early and took a ride on a rubber raft on the Snake River. Everyone, even Ali Baba who had passed his intermediate swimming test the summer before, had to wear bright orange life vests. It was very quiet out on the water. The splashing of the oars made the only sound. The guide told them to listen carefully. Soon they could hear the sounds of birds calling and animals grazing near the water.

"I see a bear!" Ali Baba called out. The hair stood up on his arms, and his heart began beating rapidly. It was an exciting moment, but it lasted only a second.

What Ali Baba saw wasn't a bear at all. It was a large tree stump. "I really thought it was a bear," Ali Baba

protested. He hadn't been trying to fool anyone this time. He felt silly making a mistake like that. The other people on the raft all laughed.

"It's pretty hard to find a bear around here these days," said the guide. "That stump is just the color of a bear. No wonder you got confused." Ali Baba knew he was saying that to make him feel better, but he didn't. He hadn't seen a bear, and he had been careless enough to mistake a tree stump for an animal. A good detective wouldn't do that.

"Is that a bear?" asked Mr. Bernstein a little later. Everyone on the raft turned to look. But it was the back end of a moose half hidden by a bush. Ali Baba smiled at his father. It was nice to see that other people made mistakes.

That afternoon, the family went horseback riding. Mr. Bernstein was the only one in the family who had ever ridden a horse before. Mrs. Bernstein was very nervous. Ali Baba felt a little scared himself, but he would never admit it. He wondered what would happen if a bear approached. Would it frighten his horse? Would he fall off?

"Are there any bears around here?" he asked the man in charge of the horses.

"If there were, the horses would smell them long before we could spot them," said the man. "The bears like to be left alone. They don't come where there are so many people and other animals."

So Ali Baba spent the next hour concentrating on riding and not on bears. It was a lot of fun, and he couldn't wait to go home and brag to Roger about his newest accomplishment. Still, even though he was having such a good time, Ali Baba wished he would see a bear before he went home. Perhaps he would have better luck at Yellowstone National Park, he thought as they drove to the second park.

Just as before, whenever they were driving along and they saw a group of parked cars, Mr. Bernstein would pull off along the side of the road, too. Parked cars usually meant that someone had spotted animals in the area. Ali Baba kept watching for a bear.

"Is there a bear?" Ali Baba always wanted to know.

"I saw a bear yesterday," said a boy who appeared to be a year or two older than Ali Baba.

"So did I," said Ali Baba. He was about to add that the bear he had seen turned out to be only a stump of an old tree. However, the older boy interrupted him.

"Hey, that's neat," the boy said, smiling at Ali Baba.

"It's getting really hard to see a bear around here these days. There're just a few of us who have done it. You must have good eyes, like me."

Ali Baba felt trapped. There was no way he could change his statement now.

"Aaaah, yeah," he mumbled.

"Where do you come from?" the boy asked.

"St. Paul, Minnesota," said Ali Baba. The words just flew out of his mouth even though they weren't true.

"I'm from Worthington, Ohio," the boy said. "My name's Greg. What's yours?"

Having already told two lies, even if one was not intentional, there was no way Ali Baba was going to identify himself. He couldn't even say his name was David, which was vague enough, as there were so many Davids in the United States.

"Larry," he said. The name just popped into his head. Ali Baba didn't know anyone named Larry, and he didn't know why he picked that name.

Luckily, at that moment, Greg's parents called him to get back into their car. They were ready to drive on.

"See you around," said Greg.

"Yeah," said Ali Baba, hoping that they would never meet again.

That evening at supper, there was a family with two small boys sitting at the next table in the park cafeteria.

"You know what?" one of them said to Ali Baba.

"What?"

"There's a kid around here named Barry, and he saw a bear."

"Really?" asked Ali Baba. He didn't feel he had to impress these two boys. And besides, he still felt uncomfortable about the story he made up to tell Greg.

"Yeah. He comes from St. Charles. That's in Missouri near where we live."

That made two guys who had seen bears, Greg and Barry. Ali Baba wished he had been that lucky.

The next day, Ali Baba sat eating an ice-cream cone when he was approached by a little girl of about five or six.

"Did you see any bears?" asked the girl.

"No," said Ali Baba. "Did you?"

"No. But there must be one around, 'cause some boy named Harry saw two of them."

"Really? How do you know?" asked Ali Baba.

"Some kids told me. Harry came here from St. Matthews. That's in Kentucky where I live."

Ali Baba licked his ice-cream cone thoughtfully. Either there were a lot more bears around than he had thought, or else there were no bears at all. It was a curious coincidence that Harry and Barry both came from cities that started with the word *Saint*. In fact, when he thought of it, so did Larry, the fellow he had invented. Larry came from St. Paul. Ali Baba was sure he was onto something now.

Ali Baba walked over to his father. Mr. Bernstein was comparing cameras with another man. A young girl stood beside the man, and she looked at Ali Baba. "Have you seen any bears?" he asked her.

The girl shook her head. "No," she said. "But I heard about another girl named Mary, just like me, and she saw a bear."

"I bet she lives in St. Paul or St. Matthews or somewhere like that," guessed Ali Baba.

"I don't know where she lives," said the Mary who stood along side of him.

Ali Baba started counting on his fingers: Larry, Barry, Harry, Mary. . . . He wondered how many other names there were that rhymed: Jerry, Carrie, Gary, Terry. He bet there were dozens of cities that sounded alike, too.

So when Ali Baba was ten years, two months, and seventeen days old, he returned home from a trip to Wyoming without having seen a single bear. However, he had solved a mystery that no one but he even knew existed. He had seen how a single accidental lapse from the truth had grown into a group of kids and a bunch of bears.

It was something to bear in mind for the future.

## *How to*
# Keep a Nature Log

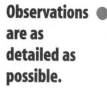

**Observations are as detailed as possible.**

**N**aturalists and nature lovers can spend hours observing wildlife. They make sketches and take notes about what they are observing. They keep this information in a nature log.

**What is a nature log?** A nature log is a record of someone's observations of living things. Each entry describes plants and animals found in one place at one time. A log contains notes, pictures, diagrams, and rubbings.

The name of the place being observed is recorded.

The date, time, and weather are noted.

I 1½"

August 6
North Hill
10:30 am
mid 70's
breezy. sunny
fields browning
over but still
lush
hear =
din of grasshoppers
song sparrow
wind in leaves
blue jay

Crab spider on
milkweed leaf
waiting for prey.
Has no web.
Changes color to suit
surroundings

broad-winged
hawk circles
over meadow.
"ke-keeeer"
call

Common
buttercup

Sketches show interesting details.

# 1 Brainstorm

**M**ake a list of nearby places where you can observe animals and plants. What about a corner of your school grounds, a park, or your backyard? A patch of grass along the sidewalk can be home to many small creatures, including insects. Choose the place that will be easiest for you to visit and observe.

## TOOLS

- pencil and notebook
- protective clothing
- magnifying glass
- reference books about animals and plants

# 2 Make a Nature Log Page

- Write the name of your observation site at the top of a notebook page.
- Label the page: "Date," "Time," and "Weather." Be sure to leave plenty of space for jotting down details and making drawings.

# 3 Observe and Record

Visit your site, and observe the living things around you for at least 20 minutes. Take notes and make sketches. Record any questions you have about what you see. When you leave, your log entry should be full of information and have at least two sketches.

**Tips**
- Remember not to pick anything that's growing.
- Be quiet. Many animals, including birds, will hide unless you keep still.
- Use your eyes, ears, and nose.

# 4 Do Research

What questions did you write in your log? What were the most fascinating plants or animals you observed? Find out more about them in encyclopedias and field guides. Write down the five most interesting facts you learned from your research. Then share your log and research with your class.

## If You Are Using a Computer . . .

Using the journal format, design a page for your nature log. The computer will automatically supply the date, but be sure to include the time and weather at the top of your entry. Then write what you have observed. Remember to include additional facts about the plants and animals you saw.

## THINK

Imagine that you are an ant on a blade of grass. What kinds of things would you see through the eyes of an ant?

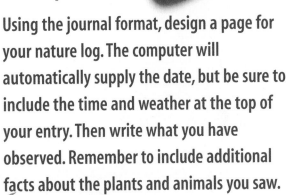

**Veronica Gonzales-Vest**
*Park Ranger* ▶

Hermit crab

Brown pelican

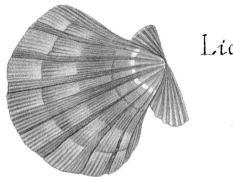

Lion's paw

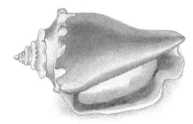

Florida fighting conch

Hibiscus

**Writers create a picture of nature through their words.**

# Wild Things

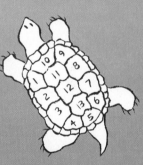

Join a young naturalist as she observes the wildlife of the Galápagos Islands.

Discover how a turtle's shell can be used as a calendar.

Read a humorous folk tale and find out how the leopard got its spots.

## WORKSHOP 2

Make a diagram of a living thing you see in its natural environment.

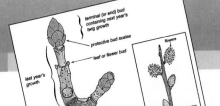

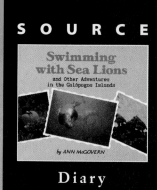

*from*

# Swimming

# with SEA LIONS

## and Other Adventures in the Galápagos Islands

### *by Ann McGovern*

The Galápagos Islands are 600 miles west of the mainland of Ecuador, South America. There are fifteen large islands and about forty small islands. Some of the small ones are just rocks jutting out of the Pacific Ocean.

*Day One*
*First day in the Galápagos!!!*
*San Cristóbal Island*

Dear Diary,

I can't believe that Grandma and I have already spent almost a whole day in the Galápagos Islands. Everything is like a strange dream.

Today I walked right up to birds and they didn't fly away! Grandma talked to sea lions—and they talked back with funny barks and burps. I've never seen such tame wild creatures in my whole life!

Living on a boat is strange, too. Our boat is called the *Mistral*. Grandma and I share a small cabin. There's a tiny bathroom in our cabin.

It's funny to think of sleeping and eating and going to the bathroom on a boat for two weeks.

The Galápagos has been a dream trip of Grandma's for years. I'm so lucky she asked me to come along.

I think I'll start from the beginning. There was snow on the ground when Grandma and I left New York. After three different plane rides, we came to these hot islands on the equator, in the Pacific Ocean!

When we landed at the little airport, we were met by Andy, our guide. I found out that every boat that travels around the Galápagos Islands has a licensed guide who knows everything about these islands and the creatures who fly, crawl, and swim here.

Grandma is keeping a diary of Andy's facts for me to add to *my* diary. I'm going to put her pages at the end. This is the symbol I'll use to show that there's more information in Grandma's diary.❋

The *Mistral*—my home for two weeks. There were eight other passengers and four crew members.

Andy says we'll spend most of our days on shore walking around the islands, looking at the creatures—mostly birds and reptiles. I asked him about swimming, my favorite sport. He said sometimes we'll swim from a beach, and sometimes we'll jump off the boat into the water.

A few people plan to scuba dive, including Grandma! She says she wants to dive with fish that are found only here. And she wants to look at hammerhead sharks, huge manta rays, and sea turtles.

I was on the ship for only an hour when I saw my first flying fish skimming just above the water.

## Still Day One Later

Dear Diary,

We are anchored close to land. Dozens of sea lions doze and sun on the shore. Others play in the water.

I jumped off the boat and got a big surprise. Even though it's broiling hot in the middle of the day, the waters of the Galápagos Islands feel real cold.

Grandma snorkeled with me. We peered down into the sea through our clear face masks. We use snorkel tubes for breathing, and the fins on our feet make it easy to swim.

51

I saw yellow-tailed surgeonfish beneath me—there must have been a hundred of them!

Suddenly a big body—then another—bolted past us. Grandma and I were quickly surrounded by *ten* adorable young sea lions!

It was a circus in the sea! Sea lion pups dived beneath us, blowing silvery bubbles through their noses. They somersaulted and flipped themselves into pretzel shapes. They chased and nipped each other. They are like big kittens. They seemed to be showing off just for us. They never scared me.

But the big male sea lion on shore did scare me with his bellowing roar! The other sea lions answered the bull with barks and coughing and burping sounds. It sounded like they were going to throw up.

Andy told us that the bull sea lions try to keep other males away. They also keep watch for sharks.

Sea lions live on almost every island so I will be seeing a lot of them. I'm glad because so far they are my most favorite creatures. ✽

I took this shot of a playful sea lion pup with an underwater camera. Isn't she adorable?

Andy didn't mind when this finch flew up and pulled out a strand of his hair. I never saw anything like that before! Andy said the bird just wanted the hair for its nest.

## Still later

Tonight I saw my first Galápagos sunset. The sky was glowing, and the sun was setting over a big rock that rose out of the sea.

## Day Two
## Santa Cruz

Dear Diary,

This morning we anchored in Academy Bay off Santa Cruz, one of the four islands in the Galápagos where people live.

I'm so excited! After lunch I'm going to see giant Galápagos tortoises—the largest land tortoises in the world! At the Charles Darwin Research Station I'll get to see them up really close. Grandma says the station was named for Charles Darwin, who sailed to the Galápagos in 1835 on the ship the *Beagle* and later became a famous scientist.

I just found out that *galápagos* means tortoise in old Spanish.

This tortoise is hiding in its shell. Maybe I scared it. (I didn't mean to.)

*Later*

Dear Diary,

I am so mad I could cry!

I read up on giant tortoises before lunch. Once there were hundreds of thousands of these huge tortoises on the Galápagos Islands.

Long ago, explorers, pirates, and seal and whale hunters came here. They stayed at sea for many months, and sometimes years. The fresh meat of the giant tortoises kept them from starving to death. The sailors knew that tortoises can stay alive for a year without food or water, so they stacked them by the hundreds in the damp, dark holds of their ships, one on top of another. Oh, those poor creatures.

Rats are no friends of tortoises, either. There were never rats here until the ships brought them. The rats swam to shore and began to destroy tortoise eggs and young tortoises. Rats are still around today. No wonder there are so few giant tortoises left.

The good news is that today there's hope for the tortoises. Andy told me that thanks to the Charles Darwin Research Station and the National Park Service, a lot of giant tortoises are being saved.

## Before bedtime

Dear Diary,

I saw them! I couldn't believe my eyes! I had read that giant tortoises can weigh over 500 pounds so I wasn't expecting a little box turtle. But I never dreamed there could be such big tortoises. And they looked so old with their great wrinkled necks and teary eyes.

At the Research Station the bigger tortoises are kept outdoors in large fenced areas, and the younger ones are in indoor pens.

My favorite tortoise is Lonesome George. Once he lived on Pinta Island with thousands of other tortoises. Hunters came to Pinta and took all the tortoises they could find. But somehow they missed one tortoise.

In 1973, workers from the Darwin Station came to Pinta Island to get rid of the wild goats that were destroying so much of the plants. The workers discovered the one tortoise that was left behind. Since he was the only one of his species left, they named him Lonesome George and brought him back to the station.

**Grandma and Marty, one of the passengers, are surrounded by giant tortoises on Santa Cruz Island.**

Spooky *scalesia* trees grow only in the Galápagos.

## Day Three
## Santa Cruz

Dear Diary,

What a day! I talked Grandma into letting me go with Andy and a few others to look for giant tortoises in the highlands.

Andy told me to wear a scarf around my neck, but it was such a hot day that I stuck it in my pocket.

We got on a rickety old bus and started our climb into the highlands. Pretty soon we were in an evergreen forest. We got out and hiked the rest of the way. The woods smelled good, like spices, but it was spooky. Strange moss hung from the branches of twisted trees.

## In the middle of the night

Dear Diary,

I can't stop worrying about tortoises. They're still in danger. Besides the goats that eat the plants and the grasses that are the tortoises' food, there are cats, dogs, pigs, rats, and donkeys that roam the islands and destroy tortoise eggs and baby tortoise hatchlings.

When I grow up, I want to work at the Charles Darwin Research Station and help save the baby tortoises.

And talk about mud! Sometimes I was almost up to my knees in muddy goo. We seemed to walk for hours—then I saw my first tortoise in the wild! I was so excited I began to shout.

I guess I shouted too loud because right away its head and feet disappeared into its shell, or *carapace* as Andy calls it. And that carapace was all any of us saw of any tortoise the whole day!

On the way back, I was feeling bad about scaring the tortoise when suddenly I felt a stinging bite on my neck. Then another, and another, till my neck felt like it was on fire!

I began to dance around like crazy. Andy ran over to me and rubbed some cooling lotion on my neck.

He told me I was being bitten by fire ants that drop from trees. If I had worn my scarf around my neck like he had told me to, they wouldn't have been able to attack me.

I squeezed my eyes shut to keep from crying. First, I scared the only tortoise we saw. Second, it was my own stupid fault that I got bitten by fire ants. And third, Andy is mad at me.

Dear Diary, you know what? I'm sorry I ever came to the Galápagos.

A giant tortoise like this can live for over 100 years.

## Later

Dear Diary,

Andy's not mad at me after all! He came up on deck of the *Mistral* where I was watching the sunset. Together we watched the sky glow and quickly turn night-black. He told me a story about a special expedition he had gone on to see the giant tortoises on Isabela Island.

With a group of people, he had hiked up to the top of the volcano where everything grows lush green and where the fog swirls so thick and wet that it drips water. The thousands of tortoises that live there aren't shy, like the Santa Cruz tortoises.

They didn't even seem to care that people were around. They just kept on munching plants.

When the tents were set up, the tortoises plodded up to inspect them. They sniffed the gear, too, and stepped on it and began to chew on it! The people had to build a fence of logs to keep the curious tortoises out of camp.

Then, Andy said, it started to pour. Dozens of tortoises came to drink the rainwater that collected in pools. Andy said it was magical.

The way he talked, I could picture the whole expedition.

I love Galápagos tortoises more than anything.

**A Galápagos sky just as the sun is setting—a sight I will never forget.**

# More About the Galápagos

**Here are a lot more facts that Grandma kept for me in her diary.**

❊ **Day One**
**More About Sea Lions, page 52**
Sea lions live in groups. One big male bull takes charge of a family of about forty females and their young. Andy says these sea lions are closely related to the California sea lions.

❊ **Day Two, Santa Cruz**
**More About Charles Darwin, page 53**
Charles Darwin was a young British naturalist whose job on a round-the-world voyage on the *Beagle* was to collect and study plants and animals.

❊ **Charles Darwin Research Station, page 54**
In 1959, the Charles Darwin Foundation was formed to protect the unusual life on the Galápagos. Scientists from all over the world come to study the plants and animals.

The Charles Darwin Research Station sends workers to different islands to collect tortoise eggs. They bring the eggs back to the station where they are protected until they hatch. Thousands of hatchlings have been raised at the station. The little tortoises are cared for until they are five years old, old enough to have a good chance of surviving in the wild. Then the tortoises are returned to their own islands where eventually they mate and produce young tortoises.

The creatures of the Galápagos are protected by rules made by the Charles Darwin Research Station and the Galápagos National Park Service.

All the guides make sure the rules are followed. Touching or feeding any of the creatures, wandering off the marked trails, or taking anything—even a broken shell or a piece of lava—is against the rules.

*from*

# Thirteen Moons on Turtle's Back

## A NATIVE AMERICAN YEAR OF MOONS

**by Joseph Bruchac and Jonathan London
illustrated by Thomas Locker**

Grandfather leaned over the long spruce log. The small boy stood close, waiting for the old man to notice him.

Grandfather looked up, a small smile on his face.

"*Kway*, Sozap," he said, "you do well at watching. Come closer. See now what I have done."

Sozap reached up to touch the carved shape of Turtle.

"How many scales are on Old Turtle's back?" Grandfather said. "*Kina* look."

Sozap counted with care.

"Thirteen," he answered.

"*Unh-hunh!*" Grandfather said, "There are always thirteen on Old Turtle's back and there are always thirteen moons in each year. Many people do not know this. They do not know, as we Abenaki know, that each moon has its own name and every moon has its own stories. I learned those stories from my grandfather. Someday, Grandson, if your memory is as sharp as your eyes, you will be able to tell them to your grandchildren."

"Grandfather," Sozap said, "do other Native people have moons, too?"

The old man nodded. "Yes, Grandson."

# Moon
# of Popping Trees

Outside the lodge,
the night air is bitter cold.
Now the Frost Giant walks
with his club in his hand.
When he strikes the trunks
of the cottonwood trees
we hear them crack
beneath the blow.
The people hide inside
when they hear that sound.

But Coyote, the wise one,
learned the giant's
magic song,
and when Coyote sang it,
the Frost Giant slept.

Now when the cottonwoods
crack with frost again
our children know, unless
they hear Coyote's song,
they must stay inside,
where the fire is bright
and buffalo robes
keep us warm.

**FIRST MOON**
*Northern Cheyenne*

# Budding Moon

One year Old Man Winter
refused to leave our land,
and so our people asked for help
from our great friend, Ju-ske-ha,
known to some as the Sun.
He knocked on the door
of Winter's lodge
then entered and sat
by Winter's cold fire.

"Leave here or you will freeze,"
Winter said,
but Ju-ske-ha breathed
and Winter grew smaller.
Ju-ske-ha waved his hand
and a white owl flew down
to carry Winter
back to the deep snow
of the north.

The lodge melted away
and the trees turned green
with new buds
as the birds began to sing.
And where the cold fire
of winter had been
was a circle of white May flowers.
So it happens each spring
when the Budding Moon comes.
All the animals wake
and we follow them
across our wide, beautiful land.

**FIFTH MOON**
*Huron*

64

# Strawberry Moon

In late spring
a small boy
whose parents had died
went hunting game
down by the river
where the Jo-ge-oh,
the Little People who care
for the plants, live.

He shared what he caught
with those Little People.
In return they took him
in a magic canoe
up into the cliffs,
taught him many things
and gave him strawberries.

He was gone just four days,
but when he returned
years had passed
and he was a tall man.
He shared with his people
what he was taught and
gave them the sweetness
of the red strawberries.
So, each year, the Senecas
sing songs of praise
to the Little People,
thanking them again
for this moon's gift.

**SIXTH MOON**
*Seneca*

# Moon of Falling Leaves

Long ago, the trees were told
they must stay awake
seven days and nights,
but only the cedar,
the pine and the spruce
stayed awake until
that seventh night.
The reward they were given
was to always be green,
while all the other trees
must shed their leaves.

So, each autumn, the leaves
of the sleeping trees fall.
They cover the floor
of our woodlands with colors
as bright as the flowers
that come with the spring.
The leaves return the strength
of one more year's growth
to the earth.

This journey
the leaves are taking
is part of that great circle
which holds us all close to the earth.

**TENTH MOON**
*Cherokee*

# Turtle's Calendar

## Thirteen Moons

1) Moon of Popping Trees

2) Baby Bear Moon

3) Maple Sugar Moon

4) Frog Moon

5) Budding Moon

6) Strawberry Moon

7) Moon When Acorns Appear

8) Moon of Wild Rice

9) Moose-Calling Moon

10) Moon of Falling Leaves

11) Moon When Deer Drop Their Horns

12) Moon When Wolves Run Together

13) Big Moon

# Authors' Note

The native people of North America have always depended upon the natural world for their survival. Watching the changes going on in the natural world with each season, they also look up into the sky and see it changing. In many parts of North America, the native people relate the cycles for the moon (called Grandmother Moon by many Native Americans) to those seasons. In every year, there are thirteen of those moon cycles, each with twenty-eight days from one new moon to the next.

Many Native American people look at Turtle's back as a sort of calendar, with its pattern of thirteen large scales standing for the thirteen moons in each year. As Grandfather says to Sozap and as an Abenaki elder said to me long ago, it reminds us that all things are connected and we must try to live in balance.

*J.B. and J.L.*

SOURCE

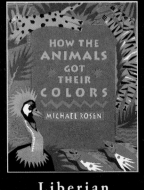

Liberian
Folk Tale

FROM

# HOW THE ANIMALS GOT THEIR COLORS

*Retold by* **MICHAEL ROSEN**
*Illustrated by* **JOHN CLEMENTSON**

# LEOPARD

See Leopard. He can leap so quick he's out of sight before you've blinked. Watch him.

See Nyomo. His eyes are so good, he can stand at the bottom of a tree and see a fly on the topmost leaf. Watch him.

You've heard of Lion? Wait for him. He comes later.

One day Leopard says to Nyomo, "Let's go, you and me, and find wild honey."

They walk, Leopard's paws pad on the ground. *Foop, foop, foop.* Nyomo's feet glide beside Leopard. *Shoo, shoo, shoo.*

"Look there!" says Leopard. "A bees' nest. I am the first to see a nest full of honey!"

They look inside. "No honey," says Nyomo. "Walk on."

They walk. *Foop, foop, foop* go Leopard's paws. *Shoo, shoo, shoo* go Nyomo's feet.

"Look there!" says Nyomo. "A bees' nest. I am the first to see a nest full of honey!"

They look inside. "Honey!" says Nyomo. "Let's eat."

They eat honey until their bellies are full and their eyes go wild. "Leopard," says Nyomo, "give yourself a name. What name do you want to call yourself?"

"Strongman," says Leopard. "And you?"

"I'm Ironman," says Nyomo. "And Ironman is a better name than Strongman."

Leopard growls, Leopard snarls, Leopard rages at that. He grabs Nyomo, ties a rope around his middle, and drags him through the forest. They meet Barking-deer.

"Say, Leopard, don't you know better than to go dragging Lion's brother along like that?" asks Barking-deer.

"I know what I know," says Leopard. "You just mind your own business, Barking-deer."

"Say, Nyomo," says Barking-deer, "will you tell me what's going on?"

"I said Ironman was a better name than Strongman, and Ironman is the name I'm going to have."

Barking-deer laughs. He laughs and laughs until it hurts. "You? Nyomo? Ironman? Little Nyomo who can't lift a log, can't bite a bone, can't even fight a fly—you call yourself Ironman in front of Leopard? You deserve everything you get."

Leopard is thinking: *Nyomo is Lion's brother. So I'll take him to Lion, and he'll tell Nyomo who's who around here.* Leopard drags Nyomo to Lion. When Lion sees his brother tied up, he is furious. Lion tells Leopard right there what to do.

"Set Nyomo free," says Lion. Leopard sets Nyomo free.

"Fetch water," says Lion. Leopard fetches water.

"Fill the bath," says Lion. Leopard fills the bath.

"Nyomo, my brother, bathe yourself in the clear, cool water." Nyomo climbs into the bath.

"Leopard, get under the bath. Stay there." Leopard gets under the bath.

Nyomo's hot, dry, dusty skin softens and shines in the bath, but the dirty water dribbles over Leopard. Leopard growls. "*Rrrr, rrrr, rrrr.*"

Now Nyomo rests. Lion and his wife bring food and sit and eat with Nyomo. They eat and eat and eat until all that's left is bits of bones, peels, and husks.

"Nyomo, dear brother," says Lion, pointing to the scraps. "Why not take these delicious little tidbits to Leopard?"

Nyomo takes bits of bones, peels, and husks to Leopard. This drives Leopard into a roaring rage.

"Lion," roars Leopard, "I'll tear you into so many pieces, it'll take ten years to count the bits."

Lion doesn't move.

"Lion, I'll throw you so high, you won't come down until next year."

Lion doesn't move.

"Lion, I'll squash you so flat, you'll blow away on the wind like a leaf."

Lion moves. Lion rises. Lion pounces on Leopard; Leopard fights back. Biting, clawing, raging. Every piece Leopard bites out of Lion, he swallows. Every piece Lion bites out of Leopard he drops on the ground.

Then, see who's coming—Old Mother. She comes near. She sees Lion and Leopard locked together, fighting in the hot dust. She sees Lion tearing at Leopard. "Run Leopard!" she cries, "Run Leopard, before Lion kills you!"

So Leopard runs. He runs and runs until he finds a pool of cool mud. With his paws, he picks up clumps of mud, and, *fap, fap, fap,* he pats them into the holes Lion made. *Fap, fap, fap,* he closes them over until there are no holes left. Then Leopard lies down to get better.

Everything's fine for Leopard now, but his skin stays spotty forever.

# How to Draw a Wildlife Diagram

**A** picture of a plant or animal provides a certain amount of information. A wildlife diagram provides more detailed information. That's why wildlife diagrams are often used to illustrate field guides and references books.

**What is a wildlife diagram?** A wildlife diagram is a detailed sketch of a plant or an animal. Like all diagrams, each part of the subject is identified with a label. A wildlife diagram also includes interesting facts about the plant or animal. These facts usually give information about the subject's habitat or feeding habits. Looking at a wildlife diagram is a quick way to get a lot of information!

# Horse Chestnut Twig

terminal (or end) bud containing next year's twig growth.

protective bud scales

leaf or flower bud

last year's growth

lenticel (breathing pore)

growth the year before

leaf stem scar

growth 3 years ago

terminal bud scar rings (where an end bud grew 2 years ago)

**Diagrams may include extra information that people might find interesting.**

**A line connects each label to the part it identifies.**

# 1 Choose an Animal or a Plant

**T**hink about the animals and plants you've seen. Is there a specific kind of bird or insect you like? Do you have a favorite kind of tree? Make a list of your favorite animals and plants. Then decide on one that you want to learn about. You may wish to pick something that can be easily observed up close.

**TOOLS**

- pencil
- ruler
- construction paper
- field guide or encyclopedia
- colored markers

# 2 Make a Diagram

**C**arefully observe the plant or animal you've selected, and draw a picture of it. You can also find a picture of it that you can trace. Then label its parts. Look through an encyclopedia, a field guide, or a nature book for help with labeling the parts. Use more than one resource to get information. Have fun with your diagram. Make it colorful by using markers.

**Tips**
- Trace a magazine photo if you are having trouble making an accurate sketch.
- Check an encyclopedia or a field guide for examples of diagrams.

# 3 Investigate Further

During your research you'll probably learn some interesting facts about the animal or plant you've chosen. How long does it live? What kinds of food does it need? Does it have any enemies? Decide on three "fascinating facts" to add to your diagram. Write them on the bottom of the page.

# 4 Classify the Diagrams

When everyone has finished, put all the diagrams together. Divide the class projects into two groups: animals and plants. For example, a diagram of a ladybug would be put in the same group as a diagram of a turtle. The class may want to turn these groupings into books.

## If You Are Using a Computer ...

Type and print out the title of your diagram and labels, using different fonts. Add clip art to illustrate the facts on the bottom of your diagram.

**THINK**

How can a diagram help a naturalist tell the difference between plants or animals that look alike?

Veronica Gonzales-Vest
*Park Ranger* ▶

Morpho butterfly

Three-toed Sloth

Passion flower

Giant armadillo

Each environment tells its own story about nature.

# Take a Hike!

Visit a suburban backyard and discover the wildlife that thrives there.

Take a walk with a nature watcher who shares his secrets for tracking and observing animals.

Join a young boy in his exciting search for a black fox.

## PROJECT

Create a field guide about the animals and plants in an outdoor place.

Scarlet macaw

Amazonia lily

My Field Guide

from
# The City Kid's Field Guide

by Ethan Herberman

## In Your Own Backyard

**D**o you know what's going on in your backyard?

A homeowner near Scranton, Pennsylvania, certainly thought he did. So when he found a man with earphones wandering around his property, he refused to believe the trespasser's excuse. The man said he was Gary Alt, a wildlife biologist for the Pennsylvania Game Commission, and that a 400-pound (180-kg) black bear tagged with a radio transmitter was living in the homeowner's hollow tree. "You're crazy!" said the homeowner. "So," says Alt, "I took a big stick, gave the tree a whump, and out popped the bear at the top.

house sparrow

dandelion

cricket

earthworm

praying mantis

raccoon

What lives in our backyards? Just the plants we put there and the animals we seek to attract? Or are there raccoons in the garbage? Rats amid the hibiscus bushes? Dandelions ducking the mower on the lawn? Quite possibly. For all species, whether they appeal to you or not, have certain basic requirements—food, water, space in which to reproduce and take cover—and these a backyard often provides.

Few black bears take advantage of the food and shelter available in human communities. But in Pennsylvania, some do and the average "backyard bear" is about 200 pounds (90 kg) heavier than its wild counterpart.

The homeowner took off. It took a long time to convince him that the bear was only there to hibernate, that it wouldn't hurt his kids."

Backyards, of course, are supposed to be private places. We plant tulips here, maples there, juniper by the fence. However, the environment we create in this way suits more than just these "invited" species. Perhaps you have heard the motto of many a self-made millionaire. "I saw my opportunities and I took 'em," they like to say— which is, as it happens, the strategy of successful living things everywhere. They find their opportunities, and they take 'em. Cottontail rabbits find your vegetable patch, dandelions your fertile lawn....

Only rarely, of course, do bears find dens in the suburbs. Even without them, however, you can turn up much that is fun and unexpected in your backyard.

### It's Green, with Eyes like a Space Alien

You wouldn't want to be a caterpillar in the flower bed when a praying mantis shows up.

You might want to be a plant, since the arrival of the mantis with its huge appetite would likely spell the end of your Japanese beetle problem—not to mention your grasshopper problem, your earwig problem....

But probably the best thing to be in relation to a praying mantis is a human being. Merely seeing an insect of its size will amaze you. It may be three inches (7.5 cm) long, so large that you can make out all the details: the triangular head, the huge round eyes, the raised-up body, the spiky forelegs.

Piece by piece, a praying mantis eats a garden spider, a fearsome hunter that was still no match for the mantis's jagged claws.

Praying mantises lay grape-sized egg cases all over town—on lawn furniture and buildings, as well as on plants. Move one to your yard, and some 200 baby mantises will soon be gobbling down everything they can grab, including each other.

These the giant holds as if in prayer, giving it its name. But it's not praying. It's hungry. Praying mantises always seem to be hungry. Watch one hunt and you are unlikely to forget the meaning of the word "predator" again.

You won't see it chase things around, though. For the most part, the mantis will do little more than wait until the motion of a nearby insect attracts its attention. Then the head swivels about, much as your head does. Sometimes the body sways, ever so slowly, in the direction of the hapless prey nearby. It may be a small insect, like a fly. On the other hand, it may be a bumblebee. But no matter. In a flash the mantis's forelegs have sprung out. Faster than your eyes can follow, the mantis has grasped its quivering victim in those jagged claws—and its former slowness returns. The victim, after all, will never escape, and the mantis has no interest in gobbling it down. Instead, it raises the insect to its mouth and bites off a piece. Finishing that one, it bites off some more.

Does it seem strange that people would buy creatures like these for their gardens? Well, think it over. Which would you prefer to remove your insect pests: mantises or a deadly insecticide spray?

The spray will work for a time. It will clear the garden of most plant-destroying insects. But a few of the pests may have a natural resistance to the poison spray. When these individuals breed, they will pass their immunity on to their young. A new population of insects that can resist the poison will grow, and before long your plants will be as infested as before.

Using insects to control each other is a safe and long-lasting way to protect your yard.

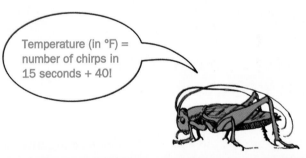

Temperature (in °F) = number of chirps in 15 seconds + 40!

## Natural Thermometers

When people start paying attention to nature, they are sometimes surprised at how much it has been telling them all along.

Take heat and cold. Many plants and animals react noticeably to changes in temperature. The rhododendron is a fine example. As the winter temperature sinks, rhododendron leaves curl down, closing up tighter and tighter to protect themselves. Keep watch on the position of those leaves when you know the temperature, and you'll soon be able to read them when you don't.

To find out how warm it is, however, you need no experience at all. Simply listen for the group singing of snowy tree crickets. You'll know you're listening to snowy tree crickets when you hear about two chirps every second. Since warmer crickets sing slightly faster than colder ones, if you count the number of cricket chirps in fifteen seconds, then add forty, you will get the approximate temperature in degrees Fahrenheit. Say you hear thirty-eight chirps in fifteen seconds. Thirty eight plus forty is seventy-eight: It's seventy-eight degrees out.

Crickets sing by rubbing their front wings together. Only male crickets do so, however. Their purpose: to attract a mate.

**rhododendron leaves**

To convert Fahrenheit to Centigrade: subtract 32, multiply by 5, divide by 9.

Every can is a treasure. A mother raccoon and her cubs dig into someone's garbage. Notice their furry "masks," powerful bodies, and banded tails. About the only items they won't eat are raw onions.

## Impawssible

"But that's impossible," you might say as you pick up the trash strewn all over the yard. "I sealed those cans firmly last night."

Any number of night roamers might have done it: skunks, squirrels, dogs, even your neighbor's cat. But if you really pressed those lids down tight, latched the box, even weighed it down with a heavy rock, then the chances are that the mess was caused by a raccoon.

And chances are it'll be back to do it again tonight.

People seem to have tried everything in their war with these large-brained animals. They've latched chicken coops, and the raccoons unlatched them; they've sealed up doorways, and the raccoons came in through the chimney; they've hung sacks of bird food on strings from trees, and the raccoons untied—didn't chew through, *untied*—the string.

Despite efforts to deter them, raccoon numbers are booming: More of them wander through some North American communities than ever prowled the same regions before the cities were built. One study turned up 150 per square mile (2.6 square km) in an Ohio suburb. They're fat, too, as you have probably seen.

To understand the raccoon's success, follow the next one you see waddling through mud or snow. Don't come too near—don't ever approach or corner a raccoon because it may carry rabies and may bite you. Instead, examine the tracks it leaves behind. Don't the forepaws look like a small child's hands? They are about that sensitive, and what's more, the raccoon is ready to take full advantage of whatever gets within its grasp.

It eats just about everything that comes its way—everything meaning berries, frogs, fish, beetles, breakfast cereal, even kittens. Like the cockroach, it has adapted well to the buildings of humans. In the wild, raccoon nests are often found in hollow trees; but in the city they have been found in sewers, culverts, garages and attics, not to mention the ventilation systems of buildings downtown.

How do raccoons pry off lids and untie string? With sensitive front paws that look much like a child's hands and leave similar imprints in mud and snow.

child's hand

raccoon's forepaw

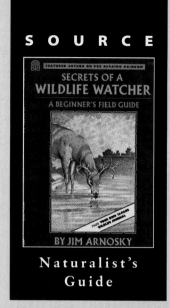

from

# SECRETS OF A
# WILDLIFE
# WATCHER

by

## JIM ARNOSKY

It was the first cold morning of winter. The ground was hard and coated with frost. I stepped briskly, following a deer path that skirted an open field. A deer had just been walking on the path. Its hoofprints were dark marks melted in the white frost. A sudden gust of bitterly cold wind whipped across the field, stinging my face. I pulled my coat collar up over my cheeks and nose. Just then I saw the deer!

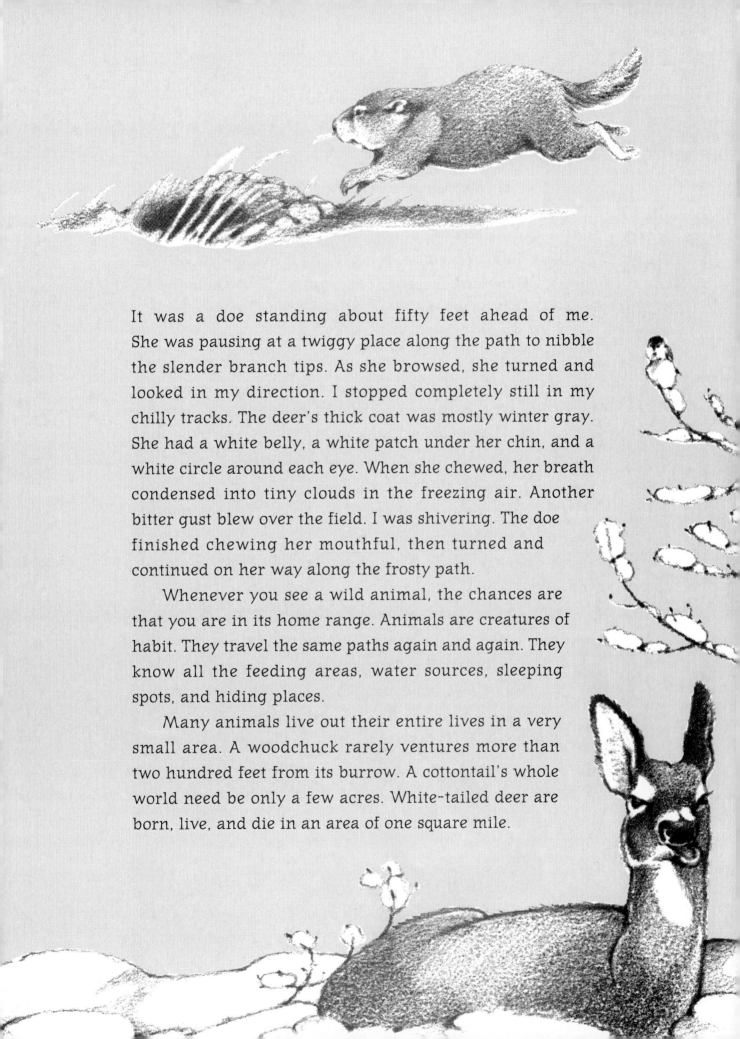

It was a doe standing about fifty feet ahead of me. She was pausing at a twiggy place along the path to nibble the slender branch tips. As she browsed, she turned and looked in my direction. I stopped completely still in my chilly tracks. The deer's thick coat was mostly winter gray. She had a white belly, a white patch under her chin, and a white circle around each eye. When she chewed, her breath condensed into tiny clouds in the freezing air. Another bitter gust blew over the field. I was shivering. The doe finished chewing her mouthful, then turned and continued on her way along the frosty path.

Whenever you see a wild animal, the chances are that you are in its home range. Animals are creatures of habit. They travel the same paths again and again. They know all the feeding areas, water sources, sleeping spots, and hiding places.

Many animals live out their entire lives in a very small area. A woodchuck rarely ventures more than two hundred feet from its burrow. A cottontail's whole world need be only a few acres. White-tailed deer are born, live, and die in an area of one square mile.

Different animals can have overlapping ranges. On one short hike in a wrinkle of a mountain, I found fresh tracks of fox, coyote, weasel, bobcat, and bear. All are predators. They are natural enemies, competing for available food. I'm sure they avoided meeting one another, but their tracks crossed, paralleled, and often followed the same trails.

A predator's home range is a hunting territory that it prowls over and over. A fox's hunting territory may cover one mile; a coyote's two or three miles. A river otter's hunting territory can stretch to twenty miles around. It takes the otter about twelve days to complete the circuit. If you remember where you have seen an animal once, you will eventually be able to see it there again.

Last summer a trio of otters included the pond behind my house in their hunting territory. Every two weeks I kept an eye on the pond, expecting them to show up. They always did. From a hiding place on the bank I watched them roll and twist acrobatically in the water. When one would dive out of sight, I would find it again by watching the line its breath bubbles made on the surface. Often the diver's wet head popped out of the water with a

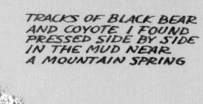

TRACKS OF BLACK BEAR AND COYOTE I FOUND PRESSED SIDE BY SIDE IN THE MUD NEAR A MOUNTAIN SPRING

gleaming trout clamped in its mouth. The otters always took trout in their front paws and ate them like candy bars, head to tail, in big, crunchy bites. Whenever they noticed me, all three would duck under water and vamoose.

Look for wildlife where water meets land, field meets wood, or lawn meets hedge. On these open "edges" sunlight stimulates a variety of plant growth that animals can eat while remaining near the safety of cover. This is why you often see animals along the roadside. They are attracted to the edges created by the road swath. The biggest white-tailed deer I've ever seen was standing on a roadside. It was a deep-bodied buck with eight long points on its antlers.

The wide ribbons of sunlit, brush-covered land on the sides of large highways are breeding grounds for small animals. Hawks take advantage of this and perch on trees, highway fencing, or road signs, and watch the ground for mice, squirrels, snakes, frogs, and songbirds. The next time you are riding in a car on a long trip, see how many hawks you can spot. Where prey animals are abundant, you may see a hawk perched along the highway every few miles or so. Learn to identify the various hawks you see.

A hawk often shares its home range with an owl. The hawk hunts it during the day. The owl hunts at night. If you have a hawk living around you, you may also have a resident owl. One of the best ways to locate it in the daytime is to search the ground under evergreen trees for "owl pellets."

An owl often swallows its food whole. Undigestible bones and hair are eventually coughed up in the form of a pellet. This happens after the owl has roosted at the end of the night. When you find an owl's pellets, there is a good chance that the owl is sleeping in the tree above them. The size of a pellet is a clue to the size and type of owl you are looking for.

BARN OWL

SCREECH OWL

ALL PELLETS
ARE SHOWN
ACTUAL SIZE

SAW-WHET OWL

RED-TAILED HAWK

PERCHES HIGH ON TOP OF DEAD TREES, POWER LINE POLES, ETC.

RED-SHOULDERED HAWK

PREFERS TO PERCH ON THE LOWER BRANCHES OF TREES

SPARROW HAWK (KESTREL)

OFTEN PERCHES ON TELEPHONE WIRES AND ROAD SIGNS

MARSH HAWK

BOTH OF THESE HAWKS PERCH NEAR THE GROUND ON FENCE POSTS, TREE STUMPS, CLUMPS OF GRASS, ETC.

ROUGH-LEGGED HAWK

RACCOON USING A TRAIL

SQUIRRELS WILL GNAW AROUND THEIR HOLE TO KEEP IT FROM GROWING CLOSED

All wild animals leave telltale signs of their activities. Look for trails tramped along the ground. If you can bend over and walk along a trail without bumping into overhanging branches and twigs, you may be on a deer trail. If you must crawl to avoid being poked, the trail has been made by smaller animals, perhaps rabbits, foxes, raccoons, or skunks. Tiny inch-wide trails are pressed by the traveling feet of mice or voles.

Examine any digs, mounds, or scratches in the ground. A squirrel leaves a small dig where it has recovered a buried nut or seed. A skunk makes numerous little holes as it digs for grubs. A mole, tunneling close to the surface, creates a line of loosened earth and a small mound wherever it surfaces. Birds scratch ground debris away while searching for insects.

Little piles of emptied nut shells or stripped pinecones are more squirrel signs. A scattering of disheveled feathers means a bird has been eaten there by a predator.

Slender branch tips and winter buds bitten off cleanly are the work of browsing deer or rabbits. Buds that have been eaten into but not bitten off the branch are chickadee peckings or the nibblings of climbing deer mice. Saplings whose bark has been gnawed are evidence of rabbits, mice, or porcupines.

SQUIRREL DIG

MOLE MOUND

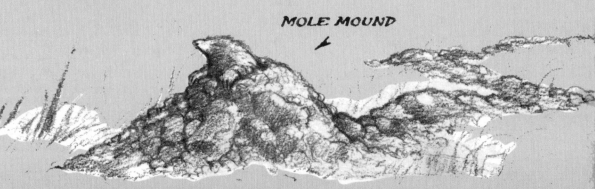

AN OPOSSUM
LIVING IN A
HOLLOW LOG
(LOOK FOR WHITE
OR SILVER HAIRS
ON LOG)

EVERGREEN
BUDS NIBBLED
INTO

A "girdle" of bare wood around the trunk of a large tree is a porcupine's doing. It has eaten all the bark from that spot. If a tree is chewed through and has fallen, you can be sure that you are in beaver territory. Beavers are the only wild animals that can fell trees.

If tree bark has been stripped or rubbed off, you will find no chew marks in the smooth, bared wood. Smooth bare spots on trees may have been made by a deer peeling the bark to eat it or, during the autumn mating season, by a feisty buck's rubbing its antlers on the tree.

Woodpeckers peck into trees to find and eat wood-boring insects. As the birds hammer, they knock away chips of wood. Look for little pieces of wood scattered on the ground around a tree. Then look up for the holes the chips came from.

When you find a hole in a tree, never reach inside. It could be a den tree, and you may get bitten by an animal who lives there. Do, however, look closely around the hole entrance to see if any hairs are caught on the bark. They are proof that the hole is occupied.

The surest identifying signs that animals leave are their footprints. In winter I follow the activities of the birds, mice, rabbits, foxes, coyotes, dogs, and cats around our farm. Day after day they scribble their stories in the snow. Each new snowfall hides a chapter of their lives.

A DOWNY
WOODPECKER
FEEDING ON
ANTS UNDER
LOOSE BARK

A YELLOW BIRCH
GIRDLED BY
A PORCUPINE

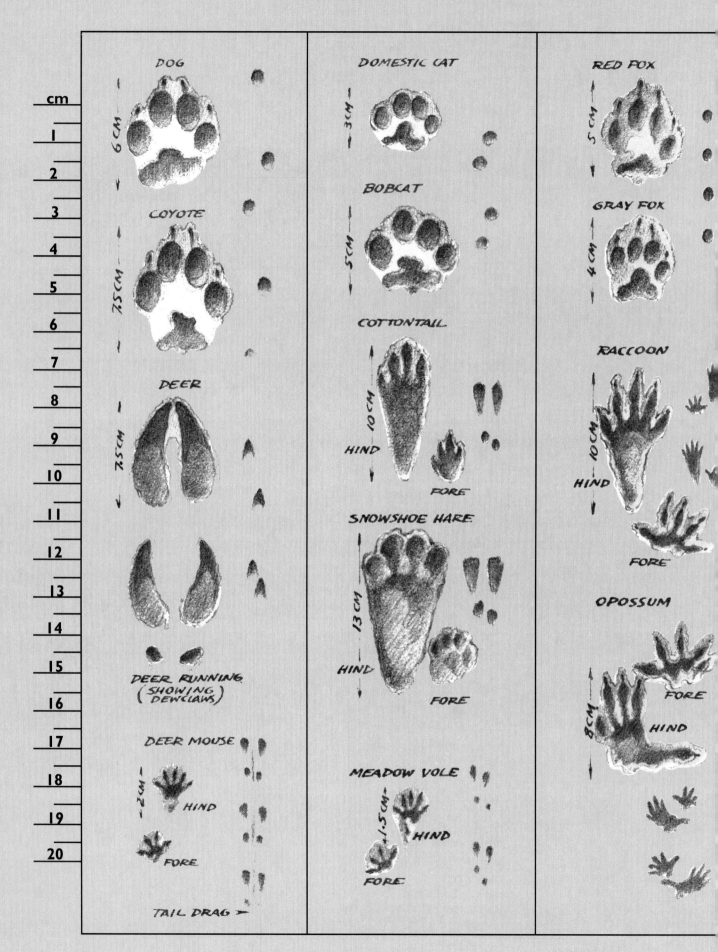

cm
1
2
3
4
5
6
7
8
9
10
11
12
13
14
15
16
17
18
19
20

DOG
6 CM

COYOTE
7.5 CM

DEER
7.5 CM

DEER RUNNING
(SHOWING DEWCLAWS)

DEER MOUSE
2 CM
HIND
FORE
TAIL DRAG ➤

DOMESTIC CAT
3 CM

BOBCAT
5 CM

COTTONTAIL
10 CM
HIND
FORE

SNOWSHOE HARE
13 CM
HIND
FORE

MEADOW VOLE
1.5 CM
HIND
FORE

RED FOX
5 CM

GRAY FOX
4 CM

RACCOON
10 CM
HIND
FORE

OPOSSUM
8 CM
FORE
HIND

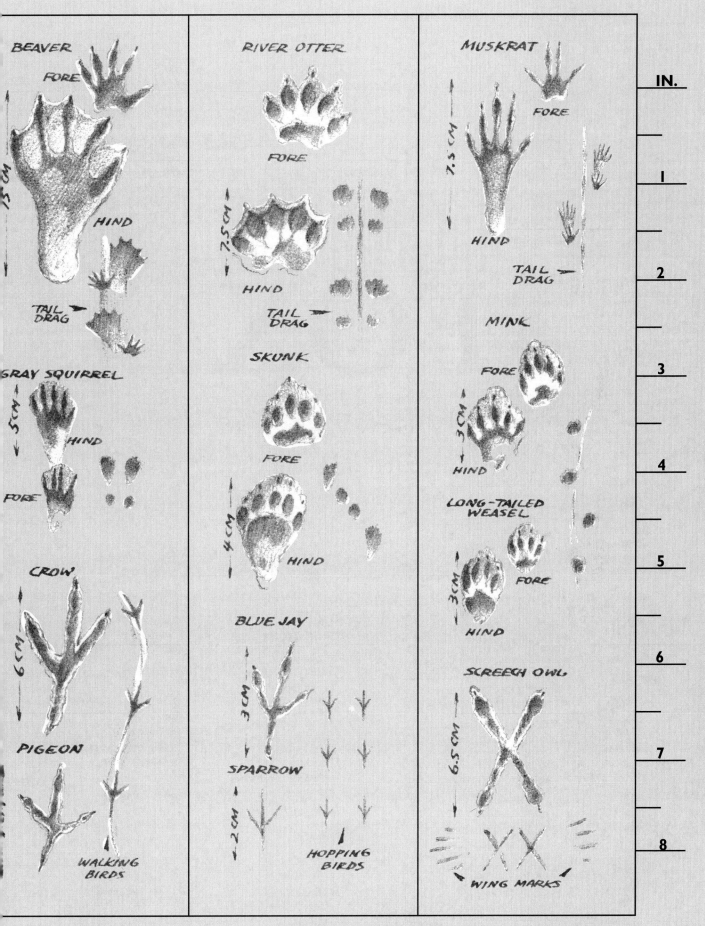

BEAVER
FORE
15 CM
HIND
TAIL DRAG

GRAY SQUIRREL
5 CM
HIND
FORE

CROW
6 CM

PIGEON

WALKING BIRDS

RIVER OTTER
FORE
7.5 CM
HIND
TAIL DRAG

SKUNK
FORE
4 CM
HIND

BLUE JAY
3 CM

SPARROW
2 CM

HOPPING BIRDS

MUSKRAT
7.5 CM
FORE
HIND
TAIL DRAG

MINK
FORE
3 CM
HIND

LONG-TAILED WEASEL
3 CM
FORE
HIND

SCREECH OWL
6.5 CM

WING MARKS

IN.

1

2

3

4

5

6

7

8

NOTE: ALL TRACKS ARE SHOWN IN SNOW

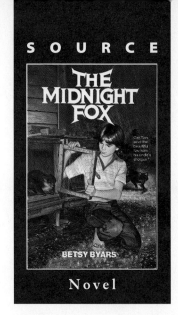

from

# THE MIDNIGHT FOX

## By Betsy Byars

### Illustrated by Peter Siu

*It's summer and Tom is visiting his aunt, uncle, and cousin Hazeline on their farm. Tom thinks he will be bored—until he sees the black fox. The next few weeks, he spends his days in the woods watching the beautiful animal.*

# THE SEARCH

The days and weeks passed quickly, long warm days in which I walked through the woods looking for the black fox.

The next time I saw her was in the late afternoon at the ravine.

This was my favorite place in the forest. The sides of the ravine were heavy dark boulders with mosses and ferns growing between the rocks, and at the bottom were trunks of old dead trees. The tree trunks were like statues in some old jungle temple, idols that had fallen and broken and would soon be lost in the creeping foliage. There was only an occasional patch of sunlight.

At the top of the ravine was a flat ledge that stuck out over the rocks, and I was lying there on my stomach this particular afternoon. The rock was warm because the sun had been on it since noon, and I was half asleep when suddenly I saw something move below me. It was the black fox. There was a certain lightness, a quickness that I could not miss.

She came over the rocks as easily as a cat. Her tail was very high and full, like a sail that was bearing her forward. Her fur was black as coal, and when she was in the shadows all I could see was the white tip of her tail.

As I watched, she moved with great ease over one of the fallen trees, ran up the other side of the ravine, and disappeared into the underbrush.

I stayed exactly where I was. My head was resting on my arms, and everything was so still I could hear the ticking of my watch. I wanted to sit up. I am sort of a bony person and after I have been lying on something hard for a long time, I get very uncomfortable. This afternoon, however, I did not move; I had the feeling that the fox was going to come back through the ravine and I did not want to miss seeing her.

While I was waiting I watched an ant run across the ledge with an insect wing. He was running so fast with this wing that he would make a little breeze and the wing would fly out of his grasp. Then he would go back and get the wing and start running again.

Then I watched some birds on the other side of the ravine circling over the rocks, catching insects as they skimmed the air. It was a beautiful sight, and I thought as I watched them, *That* is what man had in mind when he first said, "I want to fly." And I thought about some old genius working up in a remote mountain valley actually making a little flying machine that he could strap on his back like a knapsack, and this old man would come down to a big air base and he would go out on the flight line and announce to everyone, "Folks, I have invented a flying machine." There would be a silence and then everyone would start laughing as if they would never stop, and finally the Captain would pause long enough to explain to the old man that flying machines had *already* been invented, that right over there—that big silver thing with the huge wings, *that* was a flying machine, and over there, those enormous bullet-shaped things, *those* were flying machines. "Well," the old man would say, shaking his head sadly, "I won't waste no more of your time. I'll just head on home," and he would press a button on his knapsack, and silently, easy as a bird, he would lift off the ground, and skimming the air, fly toward the hills. For a moment everyone would be too stunned to move, and then the General would cry, "Come back, come back," and everyone at the air base would run beneath the flying old man crying, "Wait, wait, come back, come back!" because that was the way every one of those men really wanted to fly, free and easy and silent as a bird. But the old man, who was a little hard of hearing, would not hear their cries and would fly off into the distance and never be seen again.

Right after I stopped thinking about this, the black fox came back. She came down the rocks the same way she had gone up, her white-tipped tail as light as a plume, and I remembered a black knight I saw once in the movies who was so tall and fine and brave you could see his black plume racing ahead of all the other knights when there was a battle.

She had something in her mouth that looked like a frog—it probably was, for the creek was low now and you could always find a frog if you wanted one. She trotted on, apparently concerned only with getting the frog home, and yet I had the feeling that she was missing nothing. She passed across the ravine in a zigzag line and then started up the other side.

I did not move, and yet all at once she looked up at me. She froze for a moment, her bright eyes looking at me with curiosity rather than fear, and she cocked her head to one side, listening.

I stayed perfectly still—I was getting good at this—and we looked at each other. Then she turned away and bounded up the side of the ravine, turning at the top and disappearing into the underbrush. I felt that somewhere in

the shelter of the trees she had paused to see if I was going to follow. Perhaps she wanted me to follow so she could lead me back into the forest, but I stayed where I was. After a while, I got up and went back to the farm.

The next time I saw the fox, it was a marvelous accident. These don't happen very often in real life, but they do happen, and that's what this was. Like the time Petie and I were walking down the alley behind his house and there, on top of this lady's garbage, we saw a mayonnaise jar full of marbles—not just cat's-eye marbles but all different kinds, kinds I had never seen before. Petie and I turned them all out on the grass and first Petie chose one and then I chose one until they were all gone. And both of us right now, today, have every single one of those marbles.

This was an even better accident. For the past two weeks I had been practically tearing the woods apart looking for the den of the black fox. I had poked under rocks and logs and stuck sticks in rotted trees, and it was a wonder that some animal had not come storming out and just bitten my hand off.

I had found a hornet's nest like a huge gray shield in a tree. I had found a bird's nest, low in a bush, with five pale-blue eggs and no mother to hatch them. I had found seven places where chipmunks lived. I had found a brown owl who never moved from one certain limb of one certain tree. I had heard a tree, split by lightning years ago, suddenly topple and crash to the ground, and I ran and got there in time to see a disgruntled possum run down the broken tree and into the woods. But I did not find the place where the black fox lived.

Now, on this day, I did not go into the woods at all. I had gone up the creek where there was an old chimney, all that was left of somebody's cabin. I had asked Aunt Millie about it, but all she could remember was that some people named Bowden had worked on the farm a long time ago and had lived here. I poked around the old chimney for a while because I was hoping I would find something that had belonged to the Bowdens, and then I gave that up and walked around the bend.

I sat on a rock, perfectly still, for a long time and looked down into the creek. There were crayfish in the water—I could see them, sometimes partly hidden beneath a covering of sand, or I could see the tips of their claws at the edge of a rock. There were fish in the water so small I could almost see through them. They stayed right together, these fish, and they moved together too.

After a while I looked across the creek and I saw a hollow where there was a small clearing. There was an outcropping of rocks behind the clearing and an old log slanted against the rocks. Soft grass sloped down to the creek bank.

I don't know how long I sat there—I usually forgot about my watch when I was in the woods—but it was a long time. I was just sitting, not expecting anything or waiting for anything. And the black fox came through the bushes.

She set a bird she was carrying on the ground and gave a small yapping bark, and at once, out of a hole beneath the rocks came a baby fox.

He did not look like his mother at all. He was tiny and woolly and he had a stubby nose. He tumbled out of the hole and fell on the bird as if he had not eaten in a month. I have never seen a fiercer fight in my life than the one that baby fox gave that dead bird. He shook it, pulled it, dragged it this way and that, all the while growling and looking about to see if anyone or anything was after his prize.

The black fox sat watching with an expression of great satisfaction. Mothers in a park sometimes watch their young children with this same fond, pleased expression. Her eyes were golden and very bright as she watched the tiny fox fall over the bird, rise, and shake it.

In his frenzy he dropped the bird, picked up an older dried bird wing in its place, and ran around the clearing. Then, realizing his mistake, he returned and began to shake the bird with even greater fierceness. After a bit he made another mistake, dropping the bird by his mother's tail, and then trying to run off with that.

In the midst of all this, there was a noise. It was on the other side of the clearing, but the black fox froze. She made a faint sound, and at once the baby fox, still carrying his bird, disappeared into the den.

The black fox moved back into the underbrush and waited. I could not see her but I knew she was waiting to lead the danger, if there was any, away from her baby. After a while I heard her bark from the woods, and I got up quietly and moved back down the creek. I did not want the black fox to see me and know that I had discovered her den.

Hazeline had told me that foxes will pick up their young like cats and take them away if they think someone has discovered their den.

I wondered if this was how the black fox had come to have only one baby. Perhaps her den had been the one discovered by Mr. Hunter. Perhaps she had started to move her cubs and had got only one to safety before Mr. Hunter had arrived with his dynamite.

I decided I would never come back here to bother her. I knew I would be tempted, because already I wanted to see that baby fox play with his bird some more, but I would not do it. If I was to see the black fox again, it would be in the woods, or in the pasture, or in the ravine, but I was not going to come to the den ever again. I did not know that an awful thing was going to happen which would cause me to break this resolution.

I went home and I put a tiny little mark on the edge of my suitcase with my penknife. I did this every time I saw the black fox. There were four marks on my suitcase

now, and in the weeks to come, there were to be ten more. Fourteen times I saw the black fox and most of those fourteen she saw me too. I think she knew that I wasn't anything to be afraid of. She didn't exactly jump with joy when she saw me and she didn't trust me, but I know she was not afraid.

After I got home, my mom said, "What on earth happened to your brand-new suitcase? There are notches all over it."

And I said, "Let me see," as if I was surprised too, but if I had wanted to, I could have sat right down then and told her about every one of those notches, that this one was for when I saw the black fox carrying home a live mouse so her baby could start learning to hunt for himself, and that this one was for when I saw the fox walking down the stream, her black legs shining like silk, and this one was for when the fox passed me so closely that I could have put out my hand and touched her thick soft fur.

## *How to* Make a Field Guide

**Create** a field guide for a *close-up* look at **nature.**

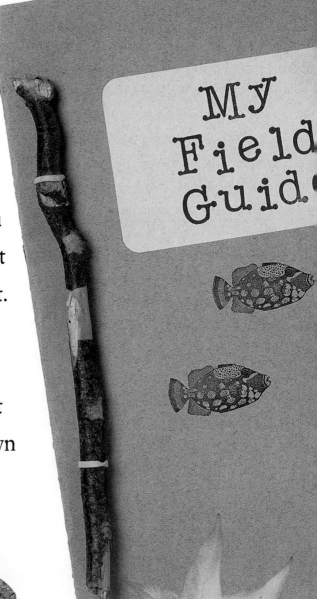

**A** field guide is a great way to manage different kinds of information. It can be a book or a pamphlet that tells about the plant and animal life in an environment. Most guides contain a collection of facts, diagrams, and pictures. They put lots of information right at your fingertips. Create your own field guide for an outdoor place.

Terns on the beach.

sea lions getting a suntan

dried seaweed

The Pacific Ocean

e design oks like a tarfish.

Scallop Shell

The sand dollar's mouth

Sand from Seal Beach

The sand dollar is a kind of sea urchin. When it's alive it has lots of short spines all over its body. These spines help it to burrow into the sand.

# 1 | Go Exploring

**Poison oak**

**D**ecide on the place you want to describe in your field guide. Before you go there, put on long pants and thick socks to protect your legs and feet from insects and poison ivy. When you get to your place, spend a few minutes just looking around. Soon you'll start to notice different plants and animals. Walk around and decide what specific area you want to describe in your guide.

**Poison ivy**

## TOOLS

- notebook and pencil

- field guides, reference books, nature magazines

- paper, colored pencils, and markers

- magnifying glass

- protective clothing

- camera (optional)

**Tips**
- Be still so you don't scare the animals.
- Concentrate on one small area at a time.
- Use encyclopedias and field guides to identify plants and animals in your environment.
- If you have a camera, take some photos of the things you are observing.

# 2 Record What You Found

Get out your notebook and list the interesting things that you see. When you're done with your list, check off at least eight items that you want to include in your field guide. Write descriptions of each item, using lots of details. Make sketches and diagrams to help you remember what things look like.

## How Am I Doing?

Before you put your field guide together, take a minute to ask yourself these questions:

- Did I write clear notes that will help me remember everything in my environment?

- Did I label my sketches?

- Have I identified the plants and animals I selected?

# 3 Make Your Guide

Now it's time to put your field guide together. Here are some ideas.

- Assembling the Pages: Attach several sheets of paper together to make a book, or fold one large sheet into thirds to create a brochure.

- The Cover: Create a title for your guide and add some art to make it come alive. Be sure to include your name.

- Pictures: Paste your sketches and diagrams onto the pages of your field guide. Having trouble drawing? Use reference books to identify the plants and animals you observed, and then trace the pictures from the books. You can also use pictures from magazines.

- Nature Facts: Write facts about each item on the pages of your book or brochure.

# 4 Present Your Guide

- Share your field guides with another class.

- Trade field guides with a friend. Visit the place someone else explored in his or her guide and see what you can learn!

## If You Are Using a Computer ...

- Print out fun captions to add to your guide.
- Make a cover with the title page maker.

**CONGRATULATIONS**

You've learned several ways to record and organize information about nature. Now you'll be an informed nature watcher!

**Veronica Gonzales-Vest**
*Park Ranger* ▶

# Glossary

**al•gae** (al′jē) *noun*
Simple plant life that lives in water. He saw green *algae* on the surface of the pond. ▲ **alga**

**al•li•ga•tor** (al′ i gā tər) *noun*
A large reptile with a long tail and a thick skin.

**boul•ders** (bōl′ dərz) *noun*
Huge rocks that are usually round and worn smooth by the wind and rain. ▲ **boulder**

**bur•row** (bur′ ō) *noun*
A hole or tunnel dug in the ground by an animal and used as shelter. The woodchuck ran into his *burrow*.

**cy•press** (sī′ prəs) *noun*
A kind of evergreen tree with small needles and woody cones.

**cypress**

**e•gret** (ē′ grit) *noun*
A kind of heron with white feathers.

**eld•er** (el′ dər) *noun*
Someone who is older and respected by the community. The mayor asked an *elder* for advice.

**en•dan•gered** (en dān′ jard) *adjective*
Threatened with extinction. Panthers are *endangered* animals.

**ex•pe•di•tion** (ek spi dish′ ən) *noun*
A long trip made for a specific purpose, such as exploration or research. They went on an *expedition* to the Antarctic.

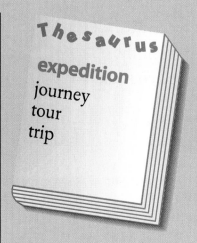
Thesaurus
**expedition**
journey
tour
trip

**fo•li•age** (fō′ lē ij) *noun*
The leaves on plants or trees.

**ham•mer•head** (ham′ ər hed) *noun*
A kind of shark that has a hammer-shaped head.

**hammerhead**

egret

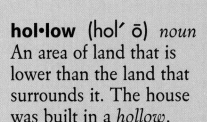

**hol·low** (hol' ō) *noun*
An area of land that is lower than the land that surrounds it. The house was built in a *hollow*.

**learned** (lurnd) *verb*
Gained knowledge through study, practice, or experience. ▲ **learn**

**ledge** (lej) *noun*
A narrow surface that sticks out from a cliff like a shelf. The bird perched on the *ledge*.

**leg·end** (lej' ənd) *noun*
An inspiring story handed down from long ago.

### Word History

**Legend** dates back to the 1300s, when it was used to mean "an inspiring story about the life of a great person." Later, it came to mean "any inspiring story from long ago." Today we use both meanings of the word.

**lodge** (loj) *noun*
A type of Native American dwelling.

### Word Study

**Memory** comes from the Latin word *memoria,* which means "memory." Several other words use the Latin root *memo.* A *memoir* is a kind of autobiography; a *memento* is a souvenir of a place or a person; and a *memorial* is something that helps people remember an important event or person.

**mem·o·ry**
(mem' ə rē) *noun*
The ability to remember things.

**moss·es**
(môs' iz) *noun*
Tiny green plants that form a covering like a mat on damp ground and rocks. ▲ **moss**

**na·tion·al park**
(nash'ə nl park) *noun*
An area of land set aside and preserved by the federal government for the public to visit.

**nat·u·ral·ist**
(nach'ər ə list) *noun*
A person who studies plants and animals.

| a | add | o͝o | took | ə = |
|---|---|---|---|---|
| ā | ace | o͞o | pool | a in *above* |
| â | care | u | up | e in *sicken* |
| ä | palm | û | burn | i in *possible* |
| e | end | yo͞o | fuse | o in *melon* |
| ē | equal | oi | oil | u in *circus* |
| i | it | ou | pout | |
| ī | ice | ng | ring | |
| o | odd | th | thin | |
| ō | open | th | this | |
| ô | order | zh | vision | |

# Glossary

**out·crop·ping**
(out′ krop ing) *noun*
The part of a rock that is above the surface of the ground. There was an *outcropping* of rocks near the lake.

**park rang·er**
(park rān′ jər) *noun*
A person whose job it is to take care of a park.

**pred·a·tor**
(pred′ ə tər) *noun*
An animal that hunts other animals for food.

**prey** (prā) *noun*
An animal that is hunted by other animals as food.

**rac·coon**
(ra ko͞on′) *noun*
A small, tree-climbing animal with black mask-like markings on its face and a bushy, ringed tail.

**range** (rānj) *noun*
An area of land on which an animal lives. The rabbit's *range* was a couple of acres.

**ra·vine** (rə vēn′) *noun*
A deep, narrow valley.

**re·search**
(ri sûrch′) *noun*
Close and careful study of a subject.

**rook·er·y**
(ro͝ok′ə rē) *noun*
A breeding place or colony of birds.

**sanc·tu·ar·ies**
(sangk′ cho͞o er ēz)
*noun*
Places where wildlife is protected and hunting is illegal. ▲ **sanctuary**

**saw grass** (sô gras)
*noun*
A kind of plant with grasslike leaves that are edged with sharp spines.

**scu·ba dive**
(sko͞o′ bə dīv) *verb*
To swim underwater wearing scuba gear.

**raccoon**

**se•quoi•a**
(si kwoi′ə) *noun*
A very tall kind of evergreen tree that grows in California and has large cones.

**site** (sīt) *noun*
The place where something is located. The Liberty Bell is a famous *site*.

**snor•kel**
(snôr′ kəl) *verb*
To swim underwater with a mask and a tube that allows breathing. The kids *snorkel* along the reef in the bay.

**ter•ri•to•ry**
(ter′ i tôr ē) *noun*
An area of land that belongs to a particular animal that defends it against other animals.

**tracks** (trakz) *noun*
Marks left by animals. The naturalist followed the rabbit's *tracks* to its burrow. ▲ **track**

**trail** (trāl) *noun*
A path.

tracks

**un•der•brush**
(un′dər brush) *noun*
Shrubs or bushes that grow under tall trees in a forest area.

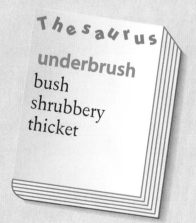
Thesaurus
**underbrush**
bush
shrubbery
thicket

**voy•age**
(voi′ ij) *noun*
A long journey, such as one made on a ship.

**wild•life**
(wīld′ līf′) *noun*
Wild plants and animals that live in their natural surroundings.

| a | add | o͝o | took | ə = |
|---|---|---|---|---|
| ā | ace | o͞o | pool | a in *above* |
| â | care | u | up | e in *sicken* |
| ä | palm | û | burn | i in *possible* |
| e | end | yo͞o | fuse | o in *melon* |
| ē | equal | oi | oil | u in *circus* |
| i | it | ou | pout | |
| ī | ice | ng | ring | |
| o | odd | th | thin | |
| ō | open | th | this | |
| ô | order | zh | vision | |

# Authors & Illustrators

**Jim Arnosky**  *pages 90–99*
When not outside fishing or hiking, this author-illustrator can usually be found at his drawing table or at work on his journals, recording wildlife discoveries.

When he talks about his book, *Secrets of a Wildlife Watcher,* he compares it to a conch shell. "The sea isn't inside the conch," he explains, "but the conch brings it to you." In the same way, he says, his book isn't filled with real trees or birds. But it still brings nature to its readers.

**Joseph Bruchac**  *pages 60–71*
When Joseph Bruchac was a small boy, his *Abenaki* grandfather taught him how to walk quietly in the woods and how to fish. His grandmother encouraged his love of reading. Bruchac says, "It wasn't until I was grown, and had children of my own, that I turned to telling traditional Native American stories. I wanted to share those stories with my sons, so I started to write them down."

Bruchac's advice to beginning writers is, "Do it a page at a time, and keep doing it. You take one step to climb a mountain."

**Betsy Byars**  *pages 100–113*

Newbery-medalist Betsy Byars has written over 25 books but her favorite is still *The Midnight Fox*. "I was walking in the woods near our cabin," she recalls, "and I came upon a fox. It wasn't a black fox, but it was a stunning moment for me. I looked at that fox, and the fox looked at me, for what seemed like an eternity—though it couldn't have been because I held my breath the whole time."

**Jean Craighead George**  *pages 10–21*

This author has studied nature her entire life. As a hobby, she cares for wild animals around her home. "These wild animals depart in autumn when they feel the urge to migrate," Jean George explains. "While they are here, however, they become characters in my stories."

**Johanna Hurwitz**  *pages 28–41*

Like Ali Baba, Johanna Hurwitz not only grew up in New York City, she's also visited national parks hoping to spot a bear. Though she never did see a bear on any of these trips, she has had better luck in her own backyard. Once she spotted a bear right outside her home in Vermont!

**Ann McGovern**  *pages 48–59*

As a child, this nature lover never imagined she would go hot-air ballooning over France.

"Because I was shy, I didn't like to speak. So, I began writing," she admits. But not anymore! Today Ann McGovern frequently gives speeches at schools and national conferences.

# Books &

*More by
Jean Craighead George*

**The Fire Bug Connection: An Ecological Mystery**
Maggie and Mitch don't know why the fire bugs are dying out. But they are determined to find out, and save these rare insects from extinction.

**One Day in the Desert**
Bird Wing, a Papago girl, and her mother live in the Sonoran Desert. What will they do when a mountain lion takes shelter in their home?

**Moon of the Deer**
What does it take for a deer to survive in the wild? This book explores the relationship between the deer and the other animals that share its habitat.

**The Adventures of Spider**
*by Joyce Arkhurst
illustrated by Jerry Pinkney*
Spider is always getting himself into and out of trouble! Here are six funny stories about this West African trickster.

**The Cricket in Times Square**
*by George Selden
illustrated by Garth Williams*
This classic novel uses humor and animal characters to tell a story about true friendship.

**A Llama in the Family**
*by Johanna Hurwitz*
Llamas are usually found in Peru. What will happen when a llama comes to live with a Vermont family?

**The Animal Atlas**
*by Barbara Taylor
illustrated by Kenneth Lilly*
This guide to the world's wildlife is packed with lifelike illustrations, helpful maps, and amazing facts.

**Crinkleroot's Guide to Knowing the Birds**
*by Jim Arnosky*
No one knows nature like Crinkleroot. In this book, he shares his secrets for identifying all kinds of birds.

**Storms**
*by Seymour Simon*
This book uses dramatic photos as well as scientific information to make it easy to understand how storms occur.

# Media

## Videos

## Software

## Magazines

### The Bear
### *Columbia Pictures*
The stars of this film are an orphaned bear cub and the huge grizzly who befriends him. Together they face many challenges, including a meeting with their most dangerous enemy: humans. (93 minutes)

### How the Leopard Got His Spots
### *Rabbit Ears*
Here's a new way of looking at an old story. This animated version of Rudyard Kipling's classic features the voice of actor Danny Glover. (30 minutes)

### Search for the Great Apes
### *National Geographic Videos*
Watch as scientist Birute Galdikas-Brindamour tries to help a baby orangutan born in captivity adjust to life in the wild. (60 minutes)

### Earthquest: Explore Ecology
### *Davidson*
Travel to a Brazilian rain forest, build food webs, solve puzzles, and more, as you learn how plants and animals live within an ecosystem.

### Mammals: A Multimedia Encyclopedia
### *National Geographic*
Use articles, sound clips, video footage, and color graphics to find information on more than 200 mammals in this unique reference source.

### Whales: Audubon Wildlife Adventures
### *Softkat*
How do whales communicate with each other? How do they find their way across the sea? Find out when you participate in four whale adventures.

### Ranger Rick
### *National Wildlife Federation*
Every issue of this award-winning magazine is packed with photos and articles about animals and their habitats.

### Zoobooks
### *Wildlife Education, Ltd.*
Each zoobook offers an in-depth look at one particular animal.

## A Place to Write
When's the best time to see geysers spout at Yellowstone? Where are the best places to hike? Find out more by requesting brochures and maps from:
National Park Service
P.O. Box 37127
Washington, D.C.
20013-7127

# Acknowledgments

Grateful acknowledgment is made to the following sources for permission to reprint from previously published material. The publisher has made diligent efforts to trace the ownership of all copyrighted material in this volume and believes that all necessary permissions have been secured. If any errors or omissions have inadvertently been made, proper corrections will gladly be made in future editions.

**Cover:** Dugald Stermer.

**Interior:** Selection and cover from THE MOON OF THE ALLIGATORS by Jean Craighead George. Text copyright © 1991 by Jean Craighead George. Illustrations copyright © 1991 by Michael Rothman. Reprinted by permission of HarperCollins Publishers.

"Alligators" and cover from OXFORD CHILDREN'S ENCYCLOPEDIA by Oxford University Press. Copyright © 1991 by Bob and Clara Calhoun. Reprinted by permission of Oxford University Press.

"Ali Baba Hunts for a Bear" and book cover from ALI BABA BERNSTEIN, LOST AND FOUND by Johanna Hurwitz, illustrated by Karen Milone. Text copyright © 1992 by Johanna Hurwitz. Cover illustration © 1992 by Karen Milone. By permission of Morrow Junior Books, a division of William Morrow & Company, Inc.

"Nature log" illustration from NATURE ALL YEAR LONG (p. 43) by Clare Walker Leslie. Copyright © 1991 by Clare Walker Leslie. By permission of Greenwillow Books, a division of William Morrow & Company, Inc.

Selection and cover from SWIMMING WITH SEA LIONS by Ann McGovern. Copyright © 1992 by Ann McGovern. Reprinted by permission of Scholastic Inc.

Selections and cover from THIRTEEN MOONS ON TURTLE'S BACK by Joseph Bruchac and Jonathan London, illustrations by Thomas Locker. Text copyright © 1992 by Joseph Bruchac and Jonathan London, illustrations copyright © 1992 by Thomas Locker, Inc. Reprinted by permission of Philomel Books.

"Leopard" text from FOLK TALES OF LIBERIA, edited by Richard Bundy, U.S. delegation to Liberia. *Journal of American Folklore* 31:121 (1918). Illustrations and cover from HOW THE ANIMALS GOT THEIR COLORS by Michael Rosen, illustrations copyright © 1992, 1991 by John Clementson. Reprinted by permission of Harcourt Brace & Company.

"Twig diagram" from NATURE ALL YEAR LONG (p. 17) by Clare Walker Leslie. Copyright © 1991 by Clare Walker Leslie. By permission of Greenwillow Books, a division of William Morrow & Company, Inc.

"In Your Own Backyard" and cover from THE CITY KID'S FIELD GUIDE by Ethan Herberman. Copyright © 1989 by Ethan Herberman and WGBH Educational Foundation. Reprinted by permission of the publisher, Simon & Schuster Books for Young Readers, New York.

Selection and cover from SECRETS OF A WILDLIFE WATCHER by Jim Arnosky. Copyright © 1983 by Jim Arnosky. Text and illustrations by permission of Lothrop, Lee & Shepard Books, cover by permission of Beech Tree Books, divisions of William Morrow & Company, Inc.

Selection and cover from THE MIDNIGHT FOX by Betsy Byars. Copyright © 1968 by Betsy Byars. Used by permission of Viking Penguin, a division of Penguin Books USA, Inc. Cover illustration used by permission of Scholastic Inc.

Cover from COME BACK, SALMON by Molly Cone, photographs by Sidnee Wheelwright. Photographs copyright © by Sidnee Wheelwright. Published by Sierra Club Books.

Cover from CHARLOTTE'S WEB by E. B. White, illustrated by Garth Williams. Illustration copyright © renewed 1980 by Garth Williams. Published by HarperCollins Publishers.

Cover from LISTENING TO CRICKETS by Candice F. Ransom, illustrated by Shelly O. Haas. Illustration copyright © 1993 by Carolrhoda Books, Inc. Published by Carolrhoda Books, Inc.

Cover from THE SECRET OF THE SEAL by Deborah Davis, illustrated by Judy Labrasca. Illustration copyright © 1989 by Judy Labrasca. Published by Crown Publishers, Inc., a division of Random House, Inc.

# Photography and Illustration Credits

**Photos:** pp. 2-3: Background © Carr Clifton. p. 4 c: © Ana Esperanza Nance for Scholastic Inc.; tc: © Art Wolfe/Tony Stone Images. p. 5 c: © Ana Esperanza Nance for Scholastic Inc.; tc: © Art Wolfe/Tony Stone Images; all others: © Richard Megna/ Fundamental Photographs for Scholastic Inc. p. 6 c: © Dean Siracusa/FPG International Corp.; tc: © Art Wolfe/Tony Stone Images; bc: ©

Scott Campbell for Scholastic Inc. pp. 22-23 bc: © Tom & Pat Leeson/DRK Photo. p. 24 tl: © Larry Lee for Scholastic Inc.; bl: Larry Lee for Scholastic Inc.; ml: Larry Lee for Scholastic Inc.; tc: © Bie Bostrom for Scholastic Inc.; tr: © Bie Bostrom for Scholastic Inc. pp. 24-25 br: © Scott Campbell for Scholastic Inc. p. 25 tr: Ana Esperanza Nance for Scholastic Inc. p. 26 c: © Bie Bostrom for Scholastic Inc.; bl: © Tom Ulrich/Tony Stone Worldwide; tc: © Bie Bostrom for Scholastic Inc.; bc: © Bie Bostrom for Scholastic Inc. pp. 26-27 br: © Geo. F. Godfrey; tr: © John Gerlack/Earth Scenes. p. 27 mr: © Scott Campbell for Scholastic Inc. p. 42 bl: © Tim Davis/Tony Stone Images; cr: © Tony Stone Images/Brian Stablyk; br: © call/Bruce Coleman, Inc. p. 43 br: © Gregory K. Scott. p. 44 c: © John Lei for Scholastic Inc. p. 45 br: © Scott Campbell for Scholastic Inc.; tr: © Comstock Red; bc: © Jim Brandenburg/Minden Pictures; bl: © Ana Esperanza Nance for Scholastic Inc. p. 76 bl: © John Lei for Scholastic Inc.; br: © Scott Campbell for Scholastic Inc. pp. 76-77 c: © John Lei for Scholastic Inc. p. 77 br: © John Lei for Scholastic Inc. p. 78 bl: © 1995, Richard Megna/ Fundamental Photographs; cr: © Hans Reinhard/ Bruce Coleman Inc. p. 79 cl: © Bruce Coleman Inc.; bl: © John Lei for Scholastic Inc. pp. 82-83 © Jack D. Teemer, Jr. p. 84 tl: © Charles Palek/Animals Animals; p. 85 br: © Photo Researchers; bl: © Walter H. Hodge/Peter Arnold. p. 88 tc: © Photo Researchers, Inc. p. 120 tc: Douglas Faulkner/Photo Researchers, Inc. pp. 120-121 br: © Doug Perrine/DRK Photo. p. 121 tr: © Lee Kuhn/FPG International Corp. p. 122 bc: © Tony Stone Images. p. 123 tr: © Walter Hodge/Peter Arnold, Inc. p. 124 cl: © courtesy of Scholastic Trade Department; bl: © Carol Bruchac. p. 125 tr (Jean Craighead George): courtesy HarperCollins Children's Books; cr (Johanna Hurwitz): © Amanda Smith; br: courtesy of Scholastic Trade Department. p. 126 bc: © Charles Krebs/The Stock Market. p. 127 cr: © Renee Lynn/Tony Stone Images; tl: © Chlaus Lotscher/Peter Arnold, Inc.; br: © Stephen Ogilvy for Scholastic Inc.

**Illustrations:** pp. 8-9: Anatoly Dverin; pp. 11-12, 15, 18-19, 21: Evangelia Philippidis; pp. 28-35, 37-41: Michele Noiset; pp. 46-47: Anatoly Dverin; pp. 80-81: Anatoly Dverin; pp. 100-101, 103-106, 108-113: Tim Lee.